BASH STREET SCHOOL

Aaargh!

OPTIMVM FACIEMVS

1938

BOP!

YEARBOOK

This yearbook belongs to...

Rargh!

SKOOL

CLASS OF 2024!
Stick your cheesy photo here!

Or draw Yourself!

BEANO

EDITOR-IN-CHIEF	Alexandria Turner
EDITOR	John Anderson
PRODUCTION EDITOR	Michelle O'Donnell
CONTENT EDITOR	Claire Bartlett
CONTENT PRODUCER	Grace Balfour-Harle
DESIGN EDITOR	Leon Strachan
DESIGNERS	Elaine Skinner
	Gary Aitchison

CONTRIBUTORS
Nigel Auchterlounie
Andy Fanton
Jess Bradley
Ned Hartley
Hugh Raine

Danny Pearson
Wayne Thompson
Laura Howell
Mel Prats
George Gant
Dave Sutherland

Barrie Appleby
The Sharp Bros.
Nigel Parkinson
Mike Donaldson
Emily McGorman-Bruce

ANGEL FACE INVESTIGATES
DETECTIVE FOR HIRE!

WELCOME TO ANGEL FACE INVESTIGATIONS...

...WE'RE THE PEOPLE TO CALL WHEN YOU CAN'T AFFORD ANYONE ELSE!

I NEED YOUR HELP!

I'VE LOST MY FAVOURITE TENNIS BALL.

WHAT DOES IT LOOK LIKE? ANY DISTINGUISHING FEATURES?

IT JUST LOOKS LIKE A TENNIS BALL REALLY.

IN THAT CASE, WE'LL FIND IT - BUT IT'LL COST YOU TWO PACKETS OF BISCUITS!

THE SEARCH STARTS IN JJ'S BEDROOM...

I'M SURPRISED SHE CAN FIND ANYTHING WITH ALL THE SPORTS STUFF IN HERE!

YEAH, IT COULD DO WITH A BIT OF A TIDY!

ONE QUICK TIDY LATER...

IT'S DEFINITELY NOT HERE! ON TO THE NEXT LOCATION!

AT LEAST IT'S A LOT TIDIER IN HERE NOW!

AT BASH STREET SCHOOL GYM...

THIS IS GETTING RIDICULOUS - THERE ARE NO TENNIS BALLS HERE EITHER!

WHAT SORT OF SCHOOL DOESN'T HAVE TENNIS BALLS?

AT BEANOTOWN TENNIS CLUB...

OW! WATCH IT! I WANT THOSE BISCUITS, BUT NOT ENOUGH TO HANG ABOUT HERE ANY LONGER!

BOUNCE!

WHERE CAN WE LOOK NEXT?

THE ONLY PLACE WE CAN... THE SHOPS!

WE'VE FOUND YOUR TENNIS BALL.

THANKS. HERE'S YOUR BISCUITS!

WAIT! YOU'VE FORGOTTEN YOUR TENNIS BALL! I SPENT ALL MY POCKET MONEY ON THAT!

AHEM... I MEAN, I SPENT ALL AFTERNOON LOOKING FOR IT!

I MADE IT ALL UP. MY MUM'S BEEN MOANING AT ME FOR AGES TO TIDY MY ROOM - AND I KNEW JENNY WOULDN'T BE ABLE TO RESIST!

OOH... *GAME, SET AND MATCH* TO YOU, JJ... BUT I STILL GOT BISCUITS!

AND I THOUGHT YOU WERE ABOUT TO RAISE A *RACKET* THERE!

THE BASH STREET KIDS

SO... HEY, MRS CREECHER! YOUR RULES ARE *STUPID!*

BUY A GOLD DESK

TODAY'S BARGAIN

WHAT? WHO DARES BESMIRCH MY RULE-MAKING?

THOSE ARE *TEACHER'S* TROUSERS! HOW VERY DARE HE!

ZOOM!

ELSEWHERE... FRESH MATHS TEXTBOOKS! I CAN ALMOST SMELL THE SUMS!

HARD SUMS

HARD SUMS

WAAH! MY MATHS!

TRIP!

GRR! *TEACHER,* EH? HE'LL PAY FOR THAT!

HARD SUMS

SO... NO, NO NO, DOM! A TEACHER WOULDN'T WALK LIKE THAT! BIG STRIDES! CHEST OUT! SHOW SOME PRIDE!

SIGH, REALLY?

THERE HE IS! I BET YOU THOUGHT IT WAS PRETTY FUNNY TO TRIP ME UP, HUH?

CHUCKLE!

YOU OWE ME AN APOLOGY!

WH-WHAT? I DIDN'T DO ANYTHING!

THANKS FOR HELPING US OUT! TEACH IS REALLY GETTING INTO *MOTION* PICTURES NOW! CHUCKLE!

A LIKELY STORY! WE SAW YOU WITH OUR OWN EYES! COME HERE!

ZOOM!

WAAH! HELP!

STAFF

DIRECTOR

CALAMITY JAMES

THE UNLUCKIEST BOY IN THE WORLD!

OH BOY! I'M *SUPER*-EXCITED TO GET MY COPY OF 'SPROUT-MAN' #1 SIGNED.

SKIP! SKIP! SKIP! SKIP!

COMIC CON WEEKLY

BEANOTOWN FILM & COMIC CON

LOOK, ALEX, NO QUEUE, IT MUST BE OUR LUCKY DAY.

BUT...

OH! IT'S BUSY. LUCKILY, ONE OF MY SUPERPOWERS IS QUEUING.

Q HERE

NOT HERE. THERE!

Queuing is a superpower?! -ED

LATER...

THIS IS RIDICULOUS. WE'VE ONLY MOVED THREE INCHES.

MANY HOURS LATER...

HERE'S YOUR WRISTBAND, WELCOME TO 'BEANOTOWN FILM AND COMIC CON'.

PHEW! I THOUGHT WE'D NEVER MAKE IT!

CREW

I WAS IN THE WRIST BAND

BLIMEY! THEY'VE GOT THE FIRST EDITION OF 'THE INCREDIBLE SULK'.

CAPTAIN WHIFF

THE FOOT

ICE-CREAM MAN

THE INCREDIBLE SULK! 1st

FIZZY

JIMMY TWO SOCKS

CHOCOLATE MOUSE

HOT ICE MAN

NOT BOY

PUKE 1

AND LOOK, 'THE AMAZING WOODLOUSE-MAN'!

BIFF!

ZOPO!

THE MASKED GRAPE

BROCCOLI MAN V SPROUT MAN

THE AMAZING WOOD LOUSE-MAN

FREE INSIDE 1000 WOOD-LICE

AMAZED!

GULP! I'M GOING TO BE LATE FOR THE SPROUT-MAN PHOTOS AND SIGNING.

SLURP! SLURP!

SPROUT-MAN SECRET CAPE POCKET

FIZZY MILK

SIGH! NOT ANOTHER QUEUE.

I guess it's time for James to use his superpower again! -ED

Sprout-Man signing and photos 2pm – 3pm

LATER...

IT'S TIME TO TOP UP MY *SUPERPOWERS* WITH A SANDWICH MUMSIE MADE ME.

WHIFF!

PONG!

GAG!

RUBI'S SCREWTOP SCIENCE

KNOCK! KNOCK!

I WONDER WHO THAT IS?

I'LL GET IT!

GOOD TO SEE YOU, PROFESSOR! I'M VERY EXCITED TO SEE WHAT YOU'VE COME UP WITH FOR ME!

RIGHT ON TIME, MR MAYOR.

DAD MUST BE DOING SOME SUPER-SECRET WORK FOR THE MAYOR! HOW EXCITING!

PRESENTING THE FASHION-BOT T-800! IT WILL CALCULATE THE BEST OUTFIT FOR YOU TO IMPRESS IN, WHETHER YOU'RE AT A DOG SHOW OR AN IMPORTANT DINNER!

OOH!

IT'S TO MAKE HIM LOOK GOOD?! WHAT A WASTE OF TIME!

LET'S GIVE IT A TRY!

TARGET ACQUIRED.

ANALYSING. RECOMMEND SOMETHING CHIC BUT NOT TOO FLASHY! BABY BLUE WILL BRING OUT THE COLOUR OF YOUR EYES!

THIS IS JUST WHAT I NEED TO IMPRESS THE... OOPS!

JUDGEMENTAL MODE ACTIVATED!

BANG!

OH NO, WHAT HAS THE MAYOR JUST KICKED?

ANALYSING. ZERO FASHION SENSE DETECTED. IMMEDIATE ACTION REQUIRED!

GULP!

BZZZT!

GAH! THIS IS SO TIGHT AND ITCHY!

OFF ON

DANGEROUS DAN
BEANOTOWN'S *TOP SPY!*

HERE WE ARE, CLASS - BUNKERTON CASTLE! THE OLDEST BUILDING IN BEANOTOWN!

URRGH! WHY CAN'T WE GO SOMEWHERE MORE EXCITING LIKE A THEME PARK? CASTLES ARE *BOOORIIIING!*

AS YOU CAN SEE, BUNKERTON HAS BEEN HOME TO THE SNOOTY FAMILY FOR CENTURIES!

I WONDER IF THEY EVER CONSIDERED GETTING A NEWER PLACE?

FOLLOW ME, CLASS... DON'T TOUCH ANYTHING ON THE WAY THROUGH! IT'S ALL VERY OLD AND VERY EXPENSIVE!

CREEEEAK!

WAAH! WHASSAT?!

WHAT'S GOING ON?

DAN! I TOLD YOU NOT TO TOUCH ANYTHING!

IT WASN'T ME!

COME ALONG! WE'VE GOT TO KEEP MOVING!

CURSES! I MISSED HIM!

I KNEW I SHOULD HAVE TAKEN THAT SUIT OF ARMOUR! THE BOSS WILL BE LIVID!

TOO RIGHT I WILL BE! WE CAN'T LET DAN SPOIL MY GREAT PLAN!

Y-YES, BOSS!

I HAVE LORD SNOOTY AND HIS PALS LOCKED UP IN HIS OWN DUNGEON, AND I SHAN'T RELEASE THEM UNTIL THE WORLD GIVES ME...

...ONE HUNDRED POUNDS!

I'VE GOT A HUNDRED POUNDS RIGHT HERE. JUST LET US OUT!

MWAH-HA-HA-HA-HA!

WHEN LITTLE ERIC EATS A BANANA, HE BECOMES...

BANANAMAN

WHAT SHOULD I SPEND MY POCKET MONEY ON?

I KNOW... *SWEETS!*

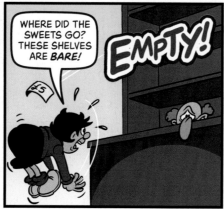

WHERE DID THE SWEETS GO? THESE SHELVES ARE *BARE!*

EMPTY!

NO SWEETS! *WAAH!*

OUTSIDE...

WHAT'S WRONG? DID YOU HEAR THE SWEET SHOP WAS OUT OF STOCK TOO?

IT'S MUCH WORSE THAN THAT - *ALL* THE SWEETS IN BEANOTOWN ARE GONE!

ARRGH! EVERYBODY PANIC!

NO SWEETS? THIS IS AN EMERGENCY FOR...

FAZOOM!

...BANANAMAN!

IT'S A GOOD THING ALL THE BANANAS WEREN'T STOLEN TOO. BURP!

HEY, KIDS, DO YOU KNOW WHERE ALL THE SWEETS IN BEANOTOWN HAVE GONE?

ALL THE SWEETS GO MISSING, SO YOU BLAME KIDS? WHAT A CHEEK!

NO, I JUST...

YOU THINK WE DID IT JUST BECAUSE WE *'BORROWED'* SOME FROM THE TEACHERS' STAFFROOM THE OTHER DAY? THAT'S SO RUDE!

LET HIM GO, TOOTS, HE'S NOT WORTH IT.

IF YOU KIDS DIDN'T STEAL ALL THE SWEETS, WHO DID?

I DON'T KNOW. ISN'T IT *YOUR* JOB AS A SUPERHERO TO FIND OUT?

I'M NOT THE SORT OF SUPERHERO WHO RELIES ON THEIR BRAIN... THINGY.

OH... MY... GOODNESS... WHAT... IS... THAT?

BEANOTOWN, PREPARE TO MEET YOUR DOOM! NO-ONE CAN STOP OUR GIANT *PINATA!*

WHAT'S A PINATA?

THIS THING! *THIS IS A PINATA!* YOU REALLY COULD HAVE GUESSED THAT FROM THE CONTEXT!

IT'S OUR, ERM... *PRESENT* TO BEANOTOWN.

YES, IT'S A PRESENT. NOTHING SUSPICIOUS HERE AT ALL!

I DUNNO, DO PEOPLE NORMALLY GIVE GIANT HORSES AS GIFTS?

YES, THAT HAS NEVER GONE WRONG IN THE HISTORY OF ANYTHING EVER.

NO, BANANAMAN! REMEMBER THE TROJAN HORSE!

UM... WAS THAT A NATURE *DOCUMENTARY?* I DON'T THINK I SAW IT.

WHEN ANCIENT GREEK SOLDIERS COULDN'T FIGHT THEIR WAY INTO THE ANCIENT CITY OF TROY, THEY BUILT A HUGE WOODEN HORSE AND LEFT IT OUTSIDE THE CITY GATES.

THE TROJANS THOUGHT IT WAS A GIFT AND OPENED THE GATES TO DRAG IT IN - THEN THE GREEK SOLDIERS HIDING INSIDE THE HUGE HORSE JUMPED OUT AND TOOK THE CITY! THE HORSE WAS A MASSIVE TRICK!

AHA! SO THIS WAS A TRICK ALL ALONG! GENERAL BLIGHT AND DOCTOR GLOOM, I'VE HAD ENOUGH OF YOUR *HORSEPLAY!*

WHAM!

OUCH! *REIN IT IN,* WILL YOU?!

CRASH!

OW!

PLUMMET!

DOOF!

DOUBLE OW!

WAIT, SO THE PLAN WASN'T TO HAVE A HORSE FULL OF NASTY SURPRISES?

NO, THE PLAN WAS TO HAVE A BIG STRONG HORSE TO WHACK YOU WITH!

DON'T YOU KNOW WHAT A PINATA IS? THIS THING IS FULL OF SWEETS! WE STOLE THEM ALL FROM BEANOTOWN!

FULL OF SWEETS?

GET IT!

HIT IT WITH STICKS!

SMASH!

HIT!

THUMP!

KEEP HITTING!

WAAH! THOSE KIDS ARE SCARY!

THIS WILL BE EASY, YOU SAID! JUST LIKE TAKING CANDY FROM A BABY, YOU SAID!

I THINK I CAN SEE WHO NEEDS SAVING HERE!

GRAB!

CAN YOU TAKE US SOMEWHERE NICE AND SAFE, LIKE PRISON?

SCOFF!

CHOMP!

MUNCH!

SOON...

RAAAH!

MORE SWEETS!

KIDS ON A SUGAR RUSH ARE WAY SCARIER THAN ANY SUPERVILLAIN! I'M GOING TO HANG OUT WITH YOU GUYS FOR A BIT.

DENNIS & GNASHER UNLEASHED

AS SEEN ON CBBC!

ARRGH! I'VE CRASHED!

CRASHED WHAT? WHERE? HOW? – ED

WHAT'S ALL THIS TALK OF CRASHING IN HERE?

I'M TRYING TO LAND MY PLANE ON AN ISLAND, BUT THE LANDING STRIP IS TOO SHORT AND ENDS IN LAVA!

I'M SO GLAD I ASKED! WHY IS IT SO DARK IN HERE? YOU AREN'T A VAMPIRE!

LEAVE THEM!

URRGH! THE SUN'S ON THE TELLY NOW!

WHEN I WAS YOUR AGE, I USED TO PLAY WITH ACTUAL THINGS IN THE REAL WORLD!

ARRGH! I'VE CRASHED AGAIN BECAUSE OF YOU! WHO PUTS LAVA NEXT TO A LANDING STRIP?!

GAME DEVELOPERS! GO AND PLAY OUTSIDE, PROVE TO ME YOU AREN'T A VAMPIRE!

COME ON, GNASHER! WE HAVE TO PLAY OUTSIDE...

...LIKE *ROMANS* OR SOMETHING.

KIDS TODAY! ALL THEY WANT IS DOWNLOADABLE THINGS! HOW DO YOU WRAP DOWNLOADABLE CONTENT FOR CHRISTMAS?

I DON'T SOUND *OLD* AT ALL!

MY TOYS WERE REAL. I HAD A PLANE... FOR FIVE MINUTES, I WONDER WHAT HAPPENED TO IT?

DAD WHEN HE WAS TEN! – ED

BEST PRESENT EVER!

IT'S RADIO-CONTROLLED, AND EXPENSIVE, SO BE CAREFUL!

DAD'S MUM AND DAD, SHE ENDS UP BEING DENNIS'S GRAN! – ED

NOT IN THE HOUSE!

SMASH!

OUTSIDE...

I'M GOING TO DO A DOUBLE TRIPLE LOOP WITH A TWIST!

WHRRRRR

SOME PEOPLE THINK DAD LOOKED LIKE DENNIS WHEN HE WAS YOUNG, BUT I CAN'T SEE IT MYSELF! – ED

INSIDE...

DO YOU THINK WE DID THE RIGHT THING GETTING DENNIS THAT?

IT'LL BE FINE, HE'S OUTSIDE WHERE HE CAN'T CAUSE ANY DAMAGE!

BETTY AND THE YETI!

THE ORDINARY GIRL WITH THE EXTRAORDINARY BEST FRIEND!

SPLOOSH!

WE'RE GETTING READY FOR 'RUFFS' - BEANOTOWN'S ANNUAL DOG SHOW!

GRUNT!

FWOOSH!

ALL CLEAN! NOW TO GET YOU NICE AND DRY.

I THINK YOU NEED A BIT OF A BRUSH.

YETI LIKE CLOUD!

YOU'VE NEVER BEEN SO CLEAN AND WELL-GROOMED... BUT YOUR TOENAILS ARE GNARLY!

HMM... WE'RE GOING TO NEED SOMETHING MUCH STRONGER!

SHUCKA-SHUCKA!

HEE-HEE! THAT TICKLE!

DAD'S TOOLBOX TO THE RESCUE!

SCRAPE! SCRAPE!

DAD'S TOOLS

THERE! YOU'RE ALL READY FOR 'RUFFS'!

BLECH!

NOW WE JUST NEED TO MAKE SURE YOU STAY CLEAN UNTIL TOMORROW.

YETI STAY CLEAN, EASY!

SCOFF!

NOM!

SLOBBER!

HOW LONG WAS THAT? TWO MINUTES?! - ED

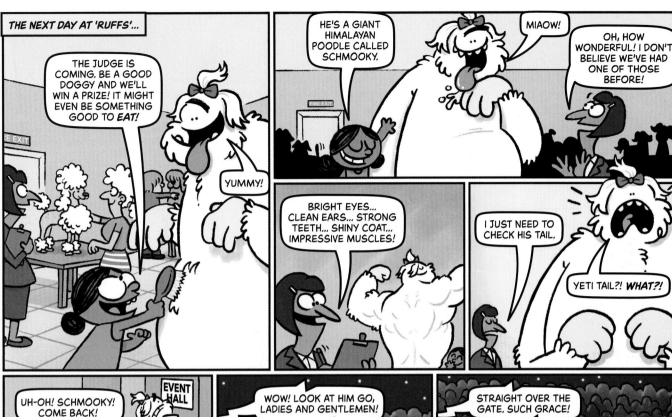

THE NEXT DAY AT 'RUFFS'...

THE JUDGE IS COMING. BE A GOOD DOGGY AND WE'LL WIN A PRIZE! IT MIGHT EVEN BE SOMETHING GOOD TO *EAT!*

YUMMY!

HE'S A GIANT HIMALAYAN POODLE CALLED SCHMOOKY.

MIAOW!

OH, HOW WONDERFUL! I DON'T BELIEVE WE'VE HAD ONE OF THOSE BEFORE!

BRIGHT EYES... CLEAN EARS... STRONG TEETH... SHINY COAT... IMPRESSIVE MUSCLES!

I JUST NEED TO CHECK HIS TAIL.

YETI TAIL?! *WHAT?!*

UH-OH! SCHMOOKY! COME BACK!

TSK! HE'LL LOSE POINTS FOR THAT!

EVENT HALL

WOW! LOOK AT HIM GO, LADIES AND GENTLEMEN!

SIT! ERM... STAY! JUST *STOP*, OKAY?!

GOOD BOY

STRAIGHT OVER THE GATE. SUCH GRACE!

CLANG!

BONY Ruffs Dog Bone Warehouse R

NO PROBLEMS WITH THE SEESAW! VERY IMPRESSIVE!

ARRGH!

SPROING!

NUT poodle

CLAP! CLAP! CLAP.

AND BEST IN SHOW IS SCHMOOKY! YOU WIN £100!

MIAOW!

GASP! £100?! WE CAN PROBABLY BUY A *WHOLE HOUSE* OR SOMETHING!

Ruffs

Pay Betty

YETI EAT PRIZE NOW.

Ruffs Date
£ 100 – 00
Betty and Schmooky
One hundred pounds only
Ruffs
***** VOID IF CHEWED *****

TODAY HAS BEEN A BIT *RUFF!*

ROGER THE DODGER
HE'S ALWAYS GOT A TRICK UP HIS SLEEVE!

AT BEANOTOWN HARBOUR...

I CAN'T BELIEVE WE WON CRUISE TICKETS! I'M LOOKING FORWARD TO THIS TRIP.

OR I WAS, UNTIL I FOUND OUT WE'D WON *THREE* TICKETS.

SLOW DOWN, YOU TWO!

I'M LOOKING FORWARD TO FEELING THE SAND BETWEEN MY TOES.

I TOLD YOU, THIS SHIP IS TAKING US TO THE FJORDS OF NORWAY.

THE FJORDS OF NORWAY?

IT'S GOING TO BE FUN LOOKING AT THE AMAZING FROZEN LANDSCAPES.

BORING! CAN'T WE JUST GO SOMEWHERE WITH A BEACH INSTEAD?

SLUMP

LATER...

SIGH! I DON'T SEE WHY WE NEED TO DRESS UP FOR DINNER.

STOP COMPLAINING, YOU LOOK VERY HANDSOME.

I LOOK LIKE A PENGUIN.

NEVER MIND, I'M LOOKING FORWARD TO THE ALL-YOU-CAN-EAT BUFFET!

I TOLD YOU, THIS IS A *FANCY* CRUISE, THERE IS NO ALL-YOU-CAN-EAT BUFFET.

SWOON!

- NO - ALL-YOU-CAN-EAT BUFFET?

SHIVER MY TIMBERS! WHAT KIND OF CRUISE IS THIS?

HOW RUDE!

DISGUSTING MANNERS.

A FREE ONE.

PFFT! I'M GOING TO GO PLAY IN THE ARCADE WHILE YOU OLDIES EAT YOUR MEALS.

ROGER, THERE IS NO ARCADE.

THAT'S IT! I WANT OFF THIS SHIP!

YOU CAN TAKE YOUR FOOD BACK TO OUR CABIN AND EAT IT THERE, ROGER.

GRUMBLE!

LATER...

NO SUN. NO SAND. NO ALL-YOU-CAN-EAT BUFFET, AND NO ARCADE...

...IT'S TIME TO CHANGE COURSE WITH DODGE 495CC.

CREW

CAPTAIN

I JUST NEED TO BORROW THIS AND THIS.

CAPTAIN ON THE BRIDGE!

WE THOUGHT YOU WERE ASLEEP, CAPTAIN.

RIGHT, YOU LOT, WE'RE CHANGING COURSE.

ARE YOU SURE, CAPTAIN? OUR GUESTS ARE EXPECTING TO SEE THE FJORDS OF NORWAY.

FOLLOW MY ORDERS OR I'LL MAKE YOU WALK THE PLANK!

GULP! CAN THE CAPTAIN MAKE US WALK THE PLANK?

I DON'T KNOW. WE'D BEST DO AS HE SAYS.

STEP ON IT!

THE NEXT MORNING...

AHOY THERE, YOU LANDLUBBERS. IT'S TIME FOR THE BEACH!

GOSH! IT'S WARM. I THOUGHT NORWAY WOULD BE COLDER.

OH NO! WHAT HAS HE DONE?

BACK ON DECK...

ARE YOU TELLING ME YOU CAN'T TELL THE DIFFERENCE BETWEEN ME AND THAT BOY DOWN THERE?!

LAST ONE TO THE BEACH HAS TO WIPE DOWN THE POOP DECK!

HARSHA'S PRANK ACADEMY

THIS TRICK IS A REAL DUMMY!

You'll need: ■ A cushion ■ A hoodie ■ A pair of trousers ■ A pair of shoes ■ A balloon ■ A felt-tip pen

1

Blow up the balloon and draw a smiley face on it.

2

Stuff the cushion into the body of the hoodie and place the balloon into the hood with the face visible.

3

Sit the hoodie on top of the toilet seat and place the trousers and shoes under it to look like a person sitting on the loo.

4

You'll feel **flushed** with success when it's discovered!

AND JJ TAKES THE GOLD!

LATER...

WOW, JJ! IS THERE ANYTHING YOU'RE *NOT* THE BEST AT?

I'M JUST LUCKY, I GUESS!

CAN I TELL YOU A SECRET, PIE FACE? I'M NOT THE BEST AT EVERYTHING. IN FACT...

...I'M A *TERRIBLE BAKER!* LOOK AT THE STATE OF THIS ECLAIR I MADE!

THAT'S AN ECLAIR? I THOUGHT IT WAS A STINKY OLD *GYM TRAINER!*

YOU'RE NOT THAT BAD, JJ! THAT DINNER YOU MADE FOR ME LAST WEEK WAS THE BEST SLICE OF SOUP I'VE EVER HAD!

SIGH... TIME FOR HOME ECONOMICS CLASS, I SUPPOSE!

SOON...

TEACHER PUT MINE IN THE OVEN FOR ME, NOW I JUST SIT AND WAIT!

YIKES! HOW LONG HAS JJ BEEN WAITING? - ED

NOT THAT LONG! I JUST GOT SOME FLOUR IN MY HAIR!

MY MACAROONS DON'T LOOK TOO GREAT!

THEY'RE MACAROONS? I THOUGHT THE GEOLOGY CLASS HAD BROUGHT SOME ROCK SAMPLES IN!

I JUST HEARD THAT THE CRICKET MATCH HAS BEEN CANCELLED. MR HEADINGTON SAYS WE'VE LOST ALL THE CRICKET BALLS!

AW, MAN!

HMM...

SO...

THANKS FOR THE CRICKET BALLS, JJ! YOU SAVED THE DAY! YOU'RE THE BEST!

WHACK!

SHHH! IT'S A SECRET, REMEMBER!

MUNCH! YOU KNOW, THIS TRAINER DOESN'T TASTE THAT BAD!

NUMSKULLS

The Little people that Live in your head! Everybody has them!

PART 1

THERE'S A LOT GOING ON IN EDD'S HEAD...

EDD IS A BIT QUIET, NICE, AND SORT OF AVERAGE...

INSIDE EDD'S HEAD...

WHY IS EDD SO AVERAGE WHEN I'M SO BRILLIANT?!

WHY IS EDD SO NICE WHEN YOU'RE SO...

EDD IS HOLDING ME BACK! THAT HAS TO BE IT. I NEVER MAKE MISTAKES!

YEAH, YOU DO.

WE'RE IN THE WRONG CLASS!

WHAT?!

I DON'T MAKE MISTAKES SO I MUST HAVE DONE THIS ON PURPOSE. I WONDER WHY?

I KNOW! WE'RE HERE BECAUSE WE'RE DITCHING EDD FOR A BETTER KID! COME ON!

THIS WILL BE EASY!

JUMP!

INSIDE DANNY'S EAR...

EAR DEPT

QUIET! I SAID, QUIET!!! DANNY'S RADAR NUMSKULL WILL BE AROUND HERE! WE DON'T WANT TO ALARM HIM! QUIET, I SAY!!!

IT'S OKAY, WE LANDED ON DANNY'S RADAR.

OF COURSE, WE DID! THAT WAS MY PLAN, PROBABLY.

EAR DEPT

IN DANNY'S BRAIN DEPARTMENT...

OOH! FANCY! AN IDEAS MACHINE.

IDEAS

DANNY'S THE LEADER SO DANNY'S BRAINY NEEDS IDEAS.

I'VE GOT AN IDEA OF MY OWN!

IS IT 'STEAL THE IDEA MACHINE AND TAKE IT BACK TO EDD'?

NO! IT'S STEAL THE IDEA MACHINE AND TAKE IT BACK TO EDD.

MAYBE EDD WOULD BE MORE SUCCESSFUL IF YOU LISTENED TO OTHER PEOPLE?

ANGEL FACE INVESTIGATES
DETECTIVE FOR HIRE!

WELCOME TO ANGEL FACE INVESTIGATIONS...

...WE SOLVE CRIMES FOR BISCUITS, BUT ONLY THE NICE ONES!

WE NEED A CRIME SOON, JENNY - OUR BISCUIT TIN IS EMPTY!

I THINK SOMEONE'S COMING UP THE STAIRS NOW.

I NEED YOUR HELP!

NO WAY! YOUR BAD LUCK ALWAYS RUBS OFF ON PEOPLE!

THINK OF THE BISCUITS, ANGEL FACE!

WHAT'S THE PROBLEM, JAMES?

I'VE LOST MY BEST FRIEND, ALEX - CAN YOU HELP FIND HIM?

FINE... MEET US AT YOUR HOUSE IN HALF AN HOUR. I'LL BRING BACKUP.

AT JAMES'S HOUSE...

GIVE GNASHER SOMETHING OF HIS TO SMELL, HE'LL BE ABLE TO FOLLOW THE SCENT AND FIND ALEX!

HERE YOU GO.

SN'FF!

ARRGH! I THINK HE'S GOT THE SCENT!

GNASH!

WAAH! STOP, GNASHER!

SPLUTCH!

I GOT THE SCENT, ALL RIGHT... THE SCENT OF SAUSAGES!

BAH! I SHOULD HAVE KNOWN BETTER THAN TO TRUST GNASHER WHEN IT'S BARBECUE SEASON!

I SAID YOUR BAD LUCK WOULD RUB OFF!

THERE HE IS!

HA! FOUND YOU, ALEX! NOW IT'S MY TURN TO HIDE!

WHAT?! I WENT THROUGH ALL OF THIS... AND A HEDGE... FOR A GAME OF HIDE-AND-SEEK? WELL, THAT JUST TAKES THE BISCUIT!

FREEWHEELING FREESTYLE FUN!

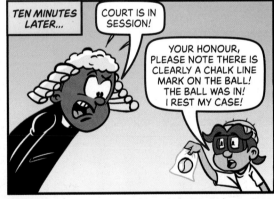

DANGEROUS DAN
BEANOTOWN'S TOP SPY!

HUH? WHAT'S WITH THAT LEVER?

SHOULD I PULL IT?

NO, THAT WOULD BE DAFT.

THEN AGAIN...

...WHAT'S THE WORST THAT COULD HAPPEN?

YANK!

UH-OH! WHAT'S HAPPENING?

WHIRR!

I'VE GOT THAT SINKING FEELING!

WHIRR!

WHERE IS THIS TAKING ME?

WELL, WELL, WELL, IF IT ISN'T AGENT DAN. WELCOME TO MY UNDERGROUND LAIR.

THE PREFECT! SO THIS IS WHERE YOU'RE HIDING!

WHIRR!

YES, IT IS! AND HOW DID YOU GET IN?

I LITERALLY JUST PULLED THAT BIG, DOPEY LEVER YOU HAD UP ON THE STREET!

YOU EXPECT ME TO BELIEVE THAT?

UM, HELLO? WHERE AM I?

SEE?!

GAH! WHY DON'T YOU ALL JUST COME IN?!

WHEN LITTLE ERIC EATS A BANANA, HE BECOMES...

BANANAMAN

I LOVE LIVING IN BEANOTOWN, EVERYONE IS SO UNIQUE!

WHAT'S UNIQUE ABOUT YOU, ERIC?

ERM... I LIKE BANANAS?

YOU NEED ANOTHER HOBBY.

IF ONLY SHE KNEW, EH, READERS?

SEE YOU LATER!

MY SECRET IS WHEN I EAT A BANANA I TURN INTO...

FAZOOM!

...BANANAMAN!

BANANAMAN! THERE YOU ARE! I'VE BEEN LOOKING FOR YOU AS PART OF MY LATEST EVIL PLAN!

POP!

THAT DOESN'T SOUND GOOD. CAN WE DO SOMETHING ELSE INSTEAD?

BUT I WANT TO USE MY NEW INVENTION!

THE MIX-O-TRON!

OOH! NICE INVENTION THIS WEEK, GENERAL BLIGHT! IT'S VERY SNAZZY!

THANKS! DOCTOR GLOOM DID MOST OF THE WORK, BUT I ADDED A CUP HOLDER AND THESE GO-FASTER STRIPES ON THE SIDE.

WHAT DOES IT DO?

IT MIXES UP PEOPLE'S POWERS! I'M GOING TO USE IT TO STEAL YOURS AND MAKE MYSELF REALLY STRONG.

BUT YOU'LL USE THOSE POWERS TO BE NAUGHTY! I KNOW YOU WILL!

GIMME ALL YOUR MONEY!

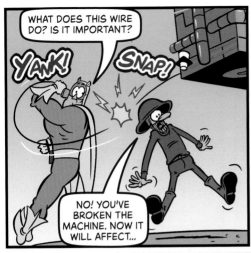

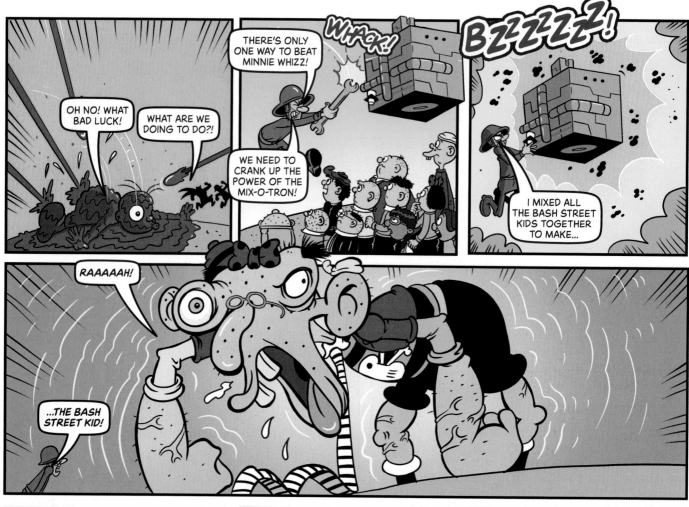

MINNIE THE MINX IN... MINX TO THE FUTURE!

PART 2

SOMEWHEN IN THE FUTURE...

WOW! BEANOTOWN LOOKS A LOT FLASHIER THAN I REMEMBER!

WELCOME TO BEANOTOWN

YEAH! I WONDER *WHEN* WE ARE?

THE YEAR IS 2054.

WHOA! THAT LAMPPOST SPOKE!

OF COURSE, I SPOKE. I AM BULB9000, THE SMARTEST LAMPPOST EVER DEVISED. MY IQ OUTSTRIPS THAT OF ANY HUMAN BEING.

OH YEAH? I BET YOU DON'T EVEN KNOW WHAT UPMIN IS!

ER... WHAT IS UPMIN?

NOTHING'S UP. *WHAT'S UP* WITH YOU? HA-HA-HA!

SIGH.

I TOTALLY GOT 'EM!

NICE ONE!

SO, WE'RE 30 YEARS INTO THE FUTURE, EH?

EVERYTHING'S SO DIFFERENT!

I BET KNOCKING A POLICE OFFICER'S HAT OFF WITH A TOMATO IS *STILL* HILARIOUS!

AHEM!

STREEETCH!

I WOULD NOT DO THAT IF I WERE YOU. IT WOULD BE AWFULLY BAD BEHAVIOUR, YOU KNOW.

THAT'S THE POINT! WHO ARE YOU, ANYWAY?

I AM *MINERVA MAKEPEACE*... AND I *DESPISE* ANY SORT OF MINXING!

GASP!

DID YOU HEAR THAT? SHE'S A PART OF MY FAMILY, BUT SHE HATES MINXING!

THE FUTURE IS ALL KINDS OF MESSED UP!

I HOPE YOU ARE NOT PLOTTING SOME SORT OF NEW MINX.

YEESH!

NO...

...I'M PLANNING THE SAME OLD MINX! CHUCKLE!

TWAAANG!

HEY!

GRR! WHO DID THAT?

LEGGIT!

IT WAS THAT HORRID GIRL HIDING IN THE BUSH!

YOU'RE IN BIG TROUBLE, YOUNG LADY...

AW! SPOILSPORT!

...I'M WRITING THIS DOWN! WHAT'S YOUR NAME?

MINNIE THE MINX!

URRGH!

AS FOR YOU, MINERVA - YOU GET A STICKER! GOOD JOB!

MY PLEASURE, SERGEANT SLIPPER!

WHAT A CRAWLER!

Good Citizen

I CAN'T BELIEVE THAT EVEN IN THE FUTURE, SLIPPER IS STILL THE WORST.

FLUTTER!

TO BE CONCLUDED!

ROGER THE DODGER
HE'S ALWAYS GOT A TRICK UP HIS SLEEVE!

TIME TO GIVE DAD THE *SLIP!*

SLIP!

POLICE BOX

WHERE ARE WE HEADING NOW?

I THINK I KNOW SOMETHING THAT WILL APPEAL TO DAD'S INNER CHILD.

SO...

WHY HAVE YOU TWO STOPPED? WHAT ARE YOU UP TO?

WE THOUGHT YOU MIGHT LIKE TO STAY A WHILE AND LOOK AT SOME OF THE 'FART WARS' COLLECTABLES.

SKID!

I'M NOT INTO ALL THAT NEW STUFF WITH THE BABY TOOTODA RUBBISH. LET'S GO.

I KNOW...

...BUT WHAT ABOUT THESE?

AND THEY'RE IN THEIR ORIGINAL PACKAGING.

WHOA! THE MILLENNIUM FARTON! ADMIRAL PARPBAR! BOGEY WAN! THEY'RE ALL HERE. I HAD THOSE WHEN I WAS A KID!

GIMME! GIMME! GIMME!

HAN! HOW YOU DOIN', YOU OLD PIRATE? SO GOOD TO SEE YOU.

ROGER, DID YOU USE A JEDI MIND TRICK?

MUM TOLD ME ONCE, NO DAD CAN RESIST THEIR CHILDHOOD TOYS. LET'S LEAVE HIM HERE.

SOON...

PEW! PEW!

SIR, YOU'VE OPENED THE PACKAGING. YOU'RE GOING TO HAVE TO PAY FOR THEM.

LATER...

I TOLD YOU TO STOP ROGER BUYING TOO MUCH JUNK - *NOT BUY IT YOURSELF!*

IT COST HOW MUCH?!

HA! DAD IS *PAYING THE COST* OF GOING BACK TO HIS CHILDHOOD.

COMIC BOOK SIGNING TODAY 11am.

MUCH ANGER I SENSE IN HIM.

HAR HAR'S JOKE SHOP!
MEET BEANOTOWN'S FUNNIEST FAMILY!

HARI · SAHANA · HEENA · HARSHA · HANI

DING-A-LING!

A CUSTOMER!

GOOD AFTERNOON, MR CHANDRA, I'M HERE TO RATE YOUR ESTABLISHMENT'S HYGIENE.

I WASN'T EXPECTING ANYONE TODAY.

NOBODY EXPECTS... *THE HYGIENE INSPECTOR!*

DUN-DUN-DUUUUUN! - ED

OH, WAIT. SHE LOOKS JUST LIKE HARSHA. I'LL PLAY ALONG WITH HER LITTLE PRANK!

MY NAME IS JEAN CLEAN, AND I WILL BE PERFORMING THE NECESSARY CHECKS.

HI, JEAN! HA-HA-HA! I GET IT! *HYGIENE!* VERY FUNNY!

I'M SORRY, I DON'T HAVE A SENSE OF HUMOUR, MR CHANDRA.

I'D BETTER NOT SHOW YOU THIS, THEN!

I'M JUST GOING TO CHECK THE SLIME FOR SIGNS OF HARMFUL INGREDIENTS THAT MIGHT CONTAMINATE YOUR FOOD ITEMS.

SQUARK!

ALL OUR SWEETS ARE SEALED IN AIRTIGHT...

...OOPS!

NO SLIME IN THESE CHOCOLATE LIMES! WOULD YOU CARE FOR ONE? THEY'RE DELICIOUS.

NO, THANK YOU, I DON'T LIKE SWEETS.

HMM... GETTING HARSHA TO COME CLEAN IS GOING TO BE HARDER THAN I THOUGHT!

DO THESE WHOOPEE CUSHIONS CONFORM TO EU SAFETY REGULATIONS?

I DON'T KNOW ABOUT THAT, BUT THEY CERTAINLY CONFORM TO *PEE-YEW* REGULATIONS! SNIGGER!

GOODNESS ME!

FRRRT!

HAVE YOU RECENTLY HAD ANY INFESTATIONS OF ANY KIND?

IT FEELS LIKE THAT WHEN THE KIDS GET HOME FROM SCHOOL!

ESPECIALLY THE MIDDLE CHILD, *HARSHA*. SHE'S A PRANKING MONSTER!

INTERESTING.

IN FACT, SHE SOMETIMES COMES DOWN HERE AND FARTS IN THE SWEETIE JARS, BURPS INTO THE WHOOPEE CUSHIONS AND FLICKS BOGIES INTO THE COSTUME WIGS!

VERY ENLIGHTENING. I'LL BE SURE TO FILE THIS REPORT IMMEDIATELY. PLEASE SIGN HERE FOR MY RECORDS.

THIS'LL MAKE HER LAUGH! I'LL SIGN IT, 'BRIAN POOPY McPOOP-FACE'!

THANK YOU, MR CHANDRA. I'LL PASS THIS ON TO MY SUPERIOR.

HI, HARSHA...

HI, DAD.

...WAIT, I-IF Y-YOU'RE HERE, TH-THEN... I J-J-JUST...

ARE YOU OKAY, DAD? YOU'RE SWEATING A LOT!

I'LL PH-PHONE THEM UP AND EXPLAIN, IT'LL BE F-F-FINE, *R-R-RIGHT?!*

AFTER ALL THAT SWEATING YOU NEED TO INSPECT YOUR *PERSONAL HYGIENE!*

HARSHA'S PRANK ACADEMY

THIS TRICK WILL MAKE A SPLASH!

You'll need: ■ A jug of water ■ A bag belonging to the person you're pranking ■ A plastic box smaller than the bag

1

Place the bag in front of you on a table.

2

Put the plastic box behind the bag where it can't be seen.

3

Stand behind the table. As the person you're pranking walks by, pour the water from the jug into the plastic box.

4

It'll look like you're pouring the water into their bag - you'll definitely have **bagging** rights with this trick!

DENNIS & GNASHER UNLEASHED

AS SEEN ON CBBC!

DENNIS HAS GONE TO VISIT GRAN BECAUSE...

BISCUIT?

DON'T MIND IF I DO!

WHAT GRAN CALLS A 'BISCUIT', EVERYONE ELSE CALLS A 'CHOCOLATE BAR'...

CHOC BLOK

THE FRONT WHEEL OF MY BIKE HAS DEVELOPED A WOBBLE. CAN YOU HELP ME FIND THE SPARE?

SURE!

IN THE GARAGE...

WHAT'S THIS THING, GRAN?

A PHONE.

THAT'S SOME WOBBLE!

POCKETS MUST HAVE BEEN *BIG* IN THE OLDEN DAYS!

HERE YOU GO, GRAN.

CAN I HAVE A LOOK THROUGH THE REST OF YOUR JUNK?

OF COURSE.

AWESOME! A RETRO 2D SIDE-SCROLLER... UNDER AN ALIEN CRYSTAL SKULL!

WHAT'S THIS?

OH... IT'S JUST A MIRROR.

GRR! WHO'S THAT DOG?!

GNASHER, NO!

HUH?!

GNASHER WENT INTO THE MIRROR! WEIRD!

ON THE OTHER SIDE...

IT'S STILL GRAN'S GARAGE... BUT TIDY!

WHAT HAPPENED TO ALL THE JUNK, GRAN?

WHAT JUNK WOULD THAT BE? BISCUIT?

I NEED TO HELP...

...WALTER?

WHERE'S THE EVIL MIRROR ME?

I'VE GOT AN IDEA!

I JUST NEED TO MAKE MYSELF LOOK LIKE THE OTHER ME!

FLATTEN

NOW TO HAVE EVIL RUBI OVERHEAR ME... ON PURPOSE!

NOW I'VE TRICKED RUBI INTO INVENTING THAT LASER-WALKER, I CAN USE IT AGAINST HER AND RULE THE TOWN!

OH YEAH?!

WHAT HE DOESN'T KNOW IS THAT I PUT A SELF-DESTRUCT BUTTON IN ALL MY INVENTIONS!

CLICK!

NEARBY...

HUH?

POP!

THAT WAS EASY! NOW THAT EVIL RUBI AND EVIL ME ARE ENEMIES, THE GOOD WALTER WILL STAND A CHANCE AGAINST THEM!

SPIKE

I CAN'T BELIEVE I JUST SAID THAT!

BACK AT OPPOSITE GRAN'S...

THERE'S THE MIRROR.

TIME TO RETURN TO OUR OWN WORLD!

THERE'S A MESS! PHEW!

ANOTHER BISCUIT, DENNIS?

THANKS, GRAN!

I GNEVER SAW OPPOSITE ME!

BACK IN THE MIRROR WORLD...

MEOW!

RUBI'S SCREWTOP SCIENCE

PIE FACE! YOU'VE GOT TO COME ROUND AND LOOK AT MY LATEST EXPERIMENT!

ON MY WAY!

I FOUND THIS FOSSIL AND ONCE I PUT IT IN MY SPECIAL DINOSAUR REGENERATION UNIT, WE SHOULD HAVE AN ACTUAL DINOSAUR! IT WILL BE REVOLUTIONARY!

UM... ISN'T THAT A VERY BAD IDEA? THERE'S A WHOLE SERIES OF FILMS ABOUT HOW BAD THIS IDEA IS!

FILMS LIKE THAT ARE *PURE FICTION!* NOTHING LIKE THAT COULD POSSIBLY GO WRONG HERE IN THE REAL WORLD!

COME ON, TRUST ME!

AND SO...

HERE WE GO! IT'S READY!

BING!

DNA-3000

AT LEAST WHATEVER IT IS MUST BE QUITE SMALL BECAUSE YOUR INVENTION IS PRETTY SM...

ROOOAAR!!

...GULP!

I DON'T WANT TO SAY THAT I TOLD YOU THIS WASN'T A GOOD IDEA, BUT...

ANGEL FACE INVESTIGATES
DETECTIVE FOR HIRE!

HELLO, THIS IS ANGEL FACE INVESTIGATIONS... IF YOU HAVE TO ASK WHAT WE DO, YOU SHOULDN'T BE ALLOWED NEAR A PHONE!

I NEED YOUR HELP. I DON'T KNOW WHO THIS PINEAPPLE BELONGS TO.

WHY DOES IT MATTER?

BECAUSE THE OWNER MIGHT BE MISSING IT!

SIGH, ALL RIGHT! I'LL FIND WHO IT BELONGS TO. THIS SHOULD BE A *PLUM* JOB!

AT REG THE VEG'S SHOP...

DOES THIS BELONG TO YOU?

NO, I DON'T SELL PINEAPPLES.

WHAT SORT OF GROCER DOESN'T SELL PINEAPPLES? THAT'S *BANANAS!*

NOW WHAT?

WHO ELSE IN BEANOTOWN IS OBSESSED WITH FRUIT?

NO, I DON'T DO PINEAPPLES OTHERWISE I'D BE CALLED PINEAPPLEMAN - AND THAT'S A TERRIBLE SUPERHERO NAME!

WORSE THAN BANANAMAN? REALLY? BUT I MAY HAVE AN IDEA WHO TO ASK NEXT...

CLOSE, BUT I LIKE MY APPLES WITHOUT PINE.

DO YOU EVEN KNOW WHAT A PINEAPPLE IS?

YES - AN APPLE THAT GROWS ON A PINE TREE!

ALL OUT OF IDEAS, ANGEL FACE AND JENNY START TO PUT UP POSTERS...

WHAT WILL WE DO IF NO-ONE EVER CLAIMS THIS LITTLE GUY?

I GUESS WE'LL HAVE TO TAKE IT HOME.

FOUND

BACK AT THE GARAGE LOFT...

ANGEL FACE - I NEED YOUR HELP!

AGAIN?! WHAT NOW?

I'VE LOST A PINEAPPLE - MY MUM SENT ME TO GET ONE FOR DESSERT AND IT'S GONE!

WAAH!

ARRGH!

EVERYTHING'S GONE A LITTLE *PEAR-SHAPED!*

JJ FREEWHEELING FREESTYLE FUN!

ALL FINISHED! HOW ARE YOU GETTING ON, JJ?

HEY, PIE FACE! I'LL BE RIGHT DOWN!

HUH?!

COME ON IN! I'LL SHOW YOU ROUND THE OLD PLACE!

WOW! YOU BUILT ALL THIS IN THE TIME IT TOOK ME TO MAKE MY LITTLE SANDCASTLE?

I WOULD HAVE BUILT A FOURTH TOWER, BUT I HURT MY SHOULDER PLAYING TENNIS YESTERDAY.

THIS IS THE LIVING ROOM. I MIGHT KNOCK THIS WALL THROUGH INTO THE KITCHEN AND MAKE IT OPEN PLAN.

IT'S LIKE AN EPISODE OF *'SAND DESIGNS'*!

ER... I THINK THAT'S 'GRAND DESIGNS', PIE FACE! - ED

WHAT ARE THE NEIGHBOURS LIKE?

THEY'RE A LITTLE *SHELLFISH* BUT THEY'RE OKAY!

HERE'S THE GAMES ROOM WITH PING PONG AND POOL TABLES, PLUS A SANDPIT! I'VE ALWAYS WANTED ONE!

LET'S HAVE A GO!

CAREFUL, YOU'RE GETTING SAND ALL OVER MY NEW FLOOR!

OOPS! SORRY!

IT'S AMAZING, JJ!

YEAH, IT'S PRETTY COOL. IT HAS ONE MAJOR PROBLEM, THOUGH...

...IT'S NOT VERY RAIN-PROOF!

NO, I *FORT* NOT!

BETTY AND THE YETI!

THE ORDINARY GIRL WITH THE EXTRAORDINARY BEST FRIEND!

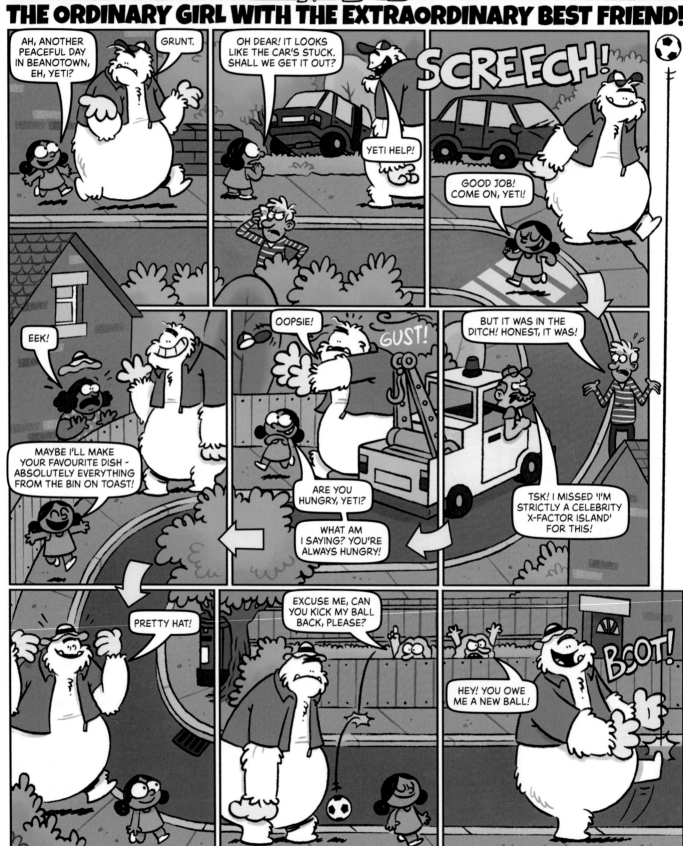

NUMSKULLS

The Little people that Live in your head! Everybody has them!

THERE'S A LOT GOING ON IN EDD'S HEAD...

...ACTUALLY, THERE ISN'T!

HELLO? ANYONE?

WHERE ARE THEY?

THEY'RE HEADED OVER TO SCOTTY'S HEAD...

THIS TIME!

JUMP!

RIGHT, I'M THE NEW BOSS IN THESE HERE PARTS AND THERE'S NOTHING YOU CAN DO ABOUT IT!

WHAT'S WITH THE TIE THINGY?

WHIPITY WHIP!

HEY! CAREFUL! THAT NIPS!

OKAY! OKAY! WE'LL LEAVE!

LASSO!

YOU WON'T LEAVE!

WE WON'T?

NO, YOU'LL BE THROWN OUT!

ARRGH!

THERE'S A LOT GOING ON IN FREDDY'S HEAD...

NOBODY MOVE!

THIS HEAD'S UNDER NEW MANAGEMENT!

CAREFUL, BRAINY! THE LAST LOT HAD SPECIAL ABILITIES! THIS ONE MIGHT TOO!

I'M GLAD YOU ASKED ABOUT MY ABILITIES.

I DIDN'T ASK, CRUNCHER ASKED!

I CAN DO GYMNASTICS!

CALAMITY JAMES

THE UNLUCKIEST BOY IN THE WORLD!

PORRIDGE SUPPLY

FUNNY, I DON'T *PEEL* ANY STRONGER.

NON-EXISTENT MUSCLE

ROLL!

RUMBLE!

I FEEL LIKE A *BANANA SPLIT!* SEEMS LIKE I CAN'T OUT-MUSCLE BAD LUCK.

ROLL!

SPLAT!

NEXT...

HA! NOW I'LL BE ABLE TO RUN FROM ANY BAD LUCK THAT COMES MY WAY!

NOT SURE THIS IS JAMES OR BILLY WHIZZ!

EXCITED SKIP!

THE ANIMALS HAVE ESCAPED FROM BEANOTOWN ZOO! RUN FOR YOUR LIFE!

CRUMBS! TIME TO PUT *MY BEST FOOT FORWARD.*

RUMBLE! THUNDER! ROAR!

OSTRICH EGG

ARRGH! MY LACES!

TRIP!

OUCH!

OUCH! I SURE CAN'T *OUTRUN* MY BAD LUCK.

SQUISH!

BILLY WHIZZ V. THE FLASH

NEXT...

HA! NO WAY BAD LUCK WOULD DARE COME AFTER ME NOW THAT I'M DRESSED LIKE DENNIS.

THAT'S GNOT MY DENNIS!

NAFF WIGS-R-US!

ALIENS ATE MY SOCKS!

SKATE!

GNASH! GNASH! GNASH!

CRIKEY! WHAT'S GOT INTO HIM?

£10000000000

WAAH!

BOOMF!

FLING!

RARE RAINBOW STRIPED SQUELCHY THING

YOU'RE LATE!

OH WELL! I GUESS I'M *STUCK* BEING ME!

BASH STREET SCHOOL

STRETCH!

THE BASH STREET KIDS

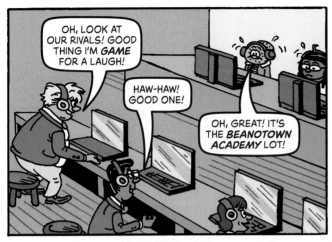

OH, LOOK AT OUR RIVALS! GOOD THING I'M *GAME* FOR A LAUGH!

HAW-HAW! GOOD ONE!

OH, GREAT! IT'S THE *BEANOTOWN ACADEMY* LOT!

MAY THE BEST TEAM WIN! AND I MEAN *US*, OF COURSE!

HAW-HAW! YOU ARE ON FIRE TODAY!

HMPH! WE'LL SHOW THEM!

I'M NANA, GAMING LEGEND! AND WE'RE HERE TO SEE TWO TEAMS FACE OFF IN A GAME OF 'OVERWASH'!

BEANOTOWN ACADEMY 00 00 BASH STREET SCHOOL

HEY, LOOK! WE'RE IN THE GAME!

OUR AVATARS ARE JUST LIKE US!

INSIDE THE GAME...

THE GAME'S STARTED! BE ON THE LOOKOUT FOR THOSE ACADEMY KIDS!

WAAH! GLUB!

SWOOSH!

HA-HA! NICELY LOOKED OUT FOR, STEVIE!

WAAH!

SWOOSH!

THERE THEY ARE!

HEY, WHERE DID HE GO? THAT WAS BANG ON TARGET!

SWOOSH!

WAAH!

SURPRISE! HAW-HAW!

SWOOSH!

HMM...

SWOOSH!

I'VE GOT IT! THEY'RE USING *CHEATS!* THAT'S THE *TELEPORTING HACK* THEY'RE USING!

DIRTY CHEATERS! GLUB!

LOOKS LIKE WE'RE WELL AHEAD, CHUMPS! YOU MAY AS WELL GO HOME! HAW-HAW!

SCOOT!

HMPH!

THEY WON'T GET AWAY WITH THIS! I'VE GOT A PLAN!

GREAT! I LOVE A PLAN!

BACK IN REALITY...

BEANOTOWN ACADEMY 30 00 BASC

HAW-HAW! WE'RE BEATING YOU 30 TO NIL.

GRR!

READY FOR MORE UPSET, URCHINS?!

LOWER

SIT DOWN!

WAAH!

OH MY! HOW FOUL!

SOUNDS LIKE IT'S YOU LOT WHO ARE *UPSET!* CHUCKLE!

PARP!

PARP!

PARP!

THAT WAS A CHEAP, TAWDRY TRICK!

RATHER! WE SHALL JUST HAVE TO CRUSH THEM IN THE GAME AS PUNISHMENT!

DS

OH YEAH?

HUH? MY CONTROLS AREN'T WORKING!

LET'S SOAK THESE *DRIPS!*

SPIN!

SOAK!

SPLASH ATTACK!

SWOOSH!

SPLOOSH!

MINE NEITHER! WHAT'S HAPPENING?

ONE ACADEMY SOAKING LATER...

AND THE BASH STREET KIDS ARE OUR WINNERS!

IT'S *GAME OVER* FOR THE ACADEMY!

GREAT IDEA TO SWAP THEIR CONTROLLERS, HARSHA!

ANGEL FACE INVESTIGATES DETECTIVE FOR HIRE!

WELCOME TO ANGEL FACE INVESTIGATIONS...

...IF THERE'S A MYSTERY, WE'LL SOLVE IT... FOR A PRICE!

ON THURSDAY...

ROGER, WHAT'S THE PROBLEM?

I HAVE TOO MUCH HOMEWORK - I NEED YOU TO DO IT FOR ME!

THAT'S NOT A MYSTERY - I'M NOT DOING YOUR HOMEWORK FOR YOU!

I'LL PAY YOU! SIX PACKETS OF BISCUITS AND A CUPCAKE!

OKAY... WOW! THAT'S A LOT! IS THIS THE WHOLE TERM'S HOMEWORK?

AND IT ALL NEEDS DONE BY MONDAY!

MONDAY?!

THE NEXT DAY AT SCHOOL...

AND ALL THIS SCIENCE HOMEWORK NEEDS DONE BY MONDAY - CAN YOU DO IT FOR TWO PACKETS OF BISCUITS?

NO PROBLEM - BUT NEXT TIME, IT'LL COST YOU DOUBLE!

THE ART HOMEWORK SHOULDN'T TAKE YOU LONG AT ALL, KHAD - YOU'RE SO GOOD AT DRAWING.

ONLY FOR A PACKET OF BISCUITS!

PLEASE, PRETTY PLEASE WITH SPRINKLES ON TOP, JJ! PLEEEAAAAASSSE!

FINE! BUT I'LL HAVE A PACKET OF BISCUITS FOR THE BOTHER!

YOU'RE SO DRAMATIC ALL THE TIME - THE DRAMA HOMEWORK WILL BE A BREEZE!

I AM AWESOME, AREN'T I? MY FOLLOWERS LOVE A GOOD DEED SO I'LL DO IT FOR ONLY TWO PACKETS OF BISCUITS!

THAT'S A GREAT DAY'S NOT-WORK DONE - OUTSOURCING IS THE WAY TO GO. NOW TO COUNT MY PAYMENT.

WHAT?! WHERE ARE MY BISCUITS!

RUBI AND STEVIE GOT TWO PACKETS EACH AND JJ AND KHAD GOT ONE TOO - THAT'S SIX PACKETS OF BISCUITS.

AT LEAST THERE'S THE CUPCAKE LEFT...

...HEY!

SORRY, THE PRICE FOR MY HELP IS ONE CUPCAKE!

THANKS FOR *MUFFIN!*

JJ FREEWHEELING FREESTYLE FUN!

PIE FACE AND I ARE GOING LARPING TODAY!

WAIT UP! I CAN'T GO FAST IN THIS, JJ!

LARP STANDS FOR 'LIVE ACTION ROLE-PLAYING', YOU PRETEND TO BE MEDIEVAL FANTASY CHARACTERS AND ACT OUT FUN ADVENTURES!

OH NO! I DIDN'T KNOW WALTER WOULD BE HERE!

WHAT HO! I AM SIR WALTER, SHERIFF OF SNOTTINGHAM!

ARRGH! 'TIS A DRAGON!

HE'S A T-REX, AREN'T YOU, PIE FACE?

ACTUALLY, I'M A TYRANNOTITAN CHUBUTENSIS FROM THE EARLY CRETACEOUS PERIOD, I MEAN... ROAR!

SPEAKETH IN OLDEN DAYS' LANGUAGE LIKE I DOTH! STAY BEHIND THAT LINE! THIS AREA IS FOR NOBLEMEN, NOT PEASANTS LIKETH YOU!

PEASANTS?!

I'VE HAD ENOUGH OF THIS! PIE FACE, HAND ME MY SPACE LASER!

SPACE LASER? THERE ARE NO SPACE LASERS IN MEDIEVAL FANTASY ROLE PLAY!

GROWL!

THERE ARE IN MY WORLD! PEW! PEW!

GRR! I CAN'T GET THE SWORD OUT OF THIS STUPID ROCK!

THAT'S IT! I'M REPORTING YOU TO THE ORGANISERS FOR NOT BEING OLDEN DAYS ENOUGH!

BUT LARPING IS ALL ABOUT HAVING FUN, WALTER!

NO, IT ISN'T!

LOOK! WALTER'S WEARING SOCKS WITH LITTLE RACE CARS ON THEM!

GASP! THEY'RE NOT *AUTHENTIC* MEDIEVAL THREADS! PUT HIM AND HIS SOCKS IN THE STOCKS!

I BEG OF THEE, SHOW MERCY!

WELL...

SO...

PEW! PEW! SEE, WALTER? IT'S MORE FUN IF YOU RELAX THE RULES A BIT, RIGHT?

THOU ART CORRECT, JJ! NOW EAT MY LIGHTSABER!

YAY!

BASH STREET SCHOOL'S 85TH ANNIVERSARY BASH!

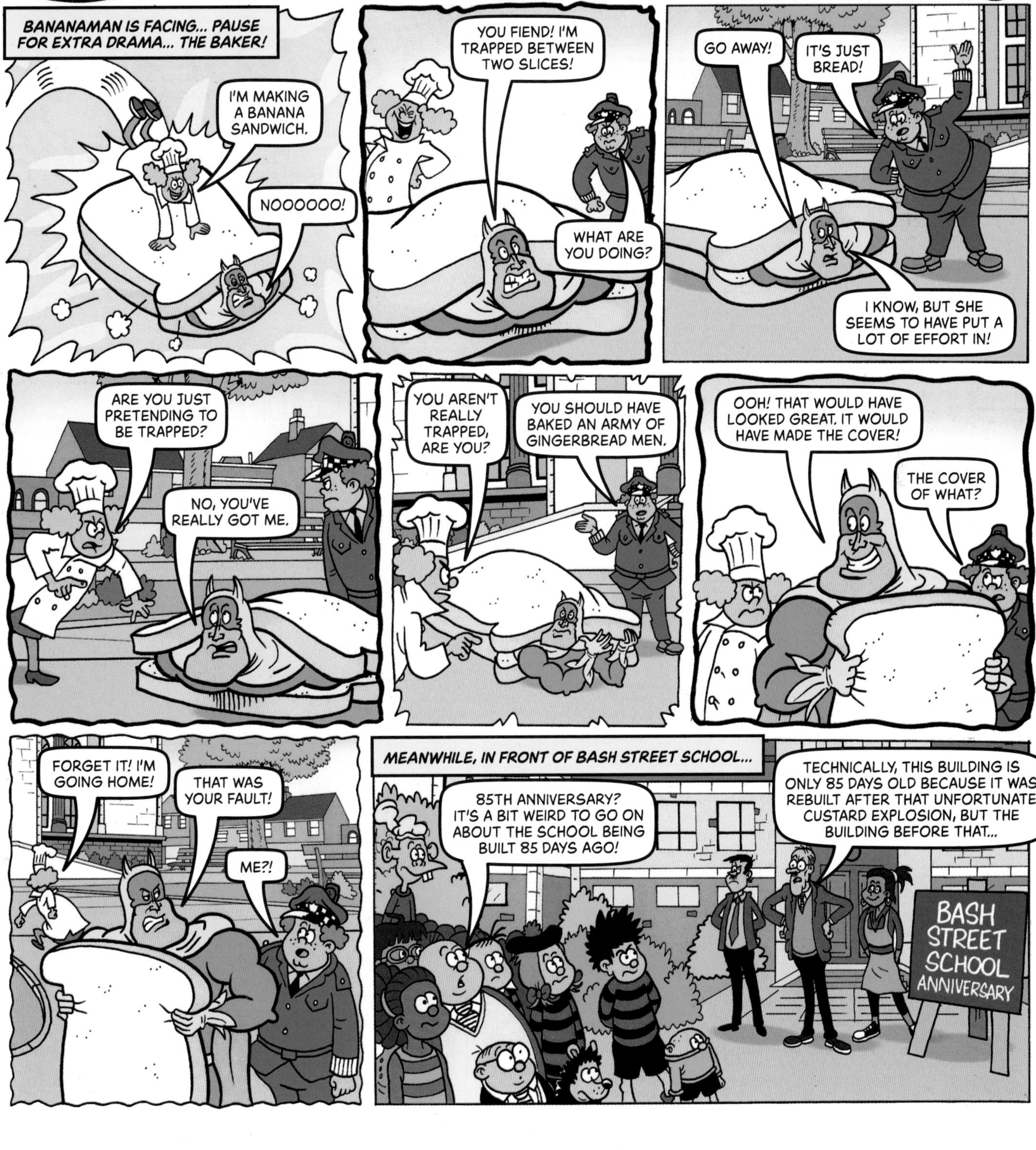

ONLY LASTED A YEAR?

OKAY, YES.

THAT SCHOOL WAS DESTROYED BY THAT GIANT MUTANT DUCK, BUT...

BANANAMAN CRASHED INTO THE SCHOOL BEFORE THAT.

AND THE ONE BEFORE THAT WAS DESTROYED BY ALIENS!

AND THE ONE BEFORE *THAT* WAS DESTROYED BY A DIFFERENT GIANT MUTANT DUCK!

ALL RIGHT! THE SCHOOL GETS WRECKED EVERY FIVE MINUTES, BUT THERE'S BEEN A SCHOOL HERE FOR 85 YEARS!

AND TO CELEBRATE, THE TEACHERS WANT TO INVITE SOME OLD PUPILS BACK FOR A REUNION!

I'VE GOT A LIST HERE...

SPLAT!!!

WHY ARE THERE SO MANY GIANT MUTANT DUCKS IN BEANOTOWN?! - ED

BUT...

HERE, DUCKY, DUCKY, DUCKY!

WHOA! LOOK AT THAT BREAD!

BANANAMAN THROWS THE BREAD OVER THE HORIZON AND THE DUCK CHASES IT...

LOB!

URRGH! THE SCHOOL'S SAFE!

BUT THE 85TH ANNIVERSARY CELEBRATIONS STILL NEED SAVING! WE'RE TOO SQUISHED TO DO IT!

WE NEED A GIANT CAKE!

AND BALLOONS!

AND I'LL COLLECT THE SPECIAL GUESTS!

PHEW! THAT'S ONE DONE!

ONLY 84, 999, 999 LEFT TO DO!

THERE, PANT... MUST BE... A WAY TO, GASP... DODGE THIS!

HEY, RUBI! CAN YOU MAKE A BALLOON-INFLATING ROBOT?

SURE!

ELSEWHERE...

HERE WE ARE - BUNKERTON CASTLE!

ECHO!

I THOUGHT THERE'D BE AN...

ECHO!

LORD SNOOTY?

THAT'S A NAME I HAVEN'T HEARD IN A LONG TIME.

HOW LONG?

NEARLY AN HOUR, DO YOU LIKE MY FAKE BEARD, BY THE WAY?

IT'S MADE FROM PURE SILVER THREAD, FEEL THE QUALITY!

RANDOM.

DO YOU WANT TO COME TO BASH STREET SCHOOL FOR THE 85TH ANNIVERSARY?

I'D LOVE TO! I OWE ALL MY SUCCESS TO BASH STREET SCHOOL...

...AND THE MILLIONS I WAS GIVEN AS A CHILD.

MEANWHILE...

HERE'S YOUR BALLOON-INFLATING ROBOT...

...B-LOON!

IT'S ADORABLE!

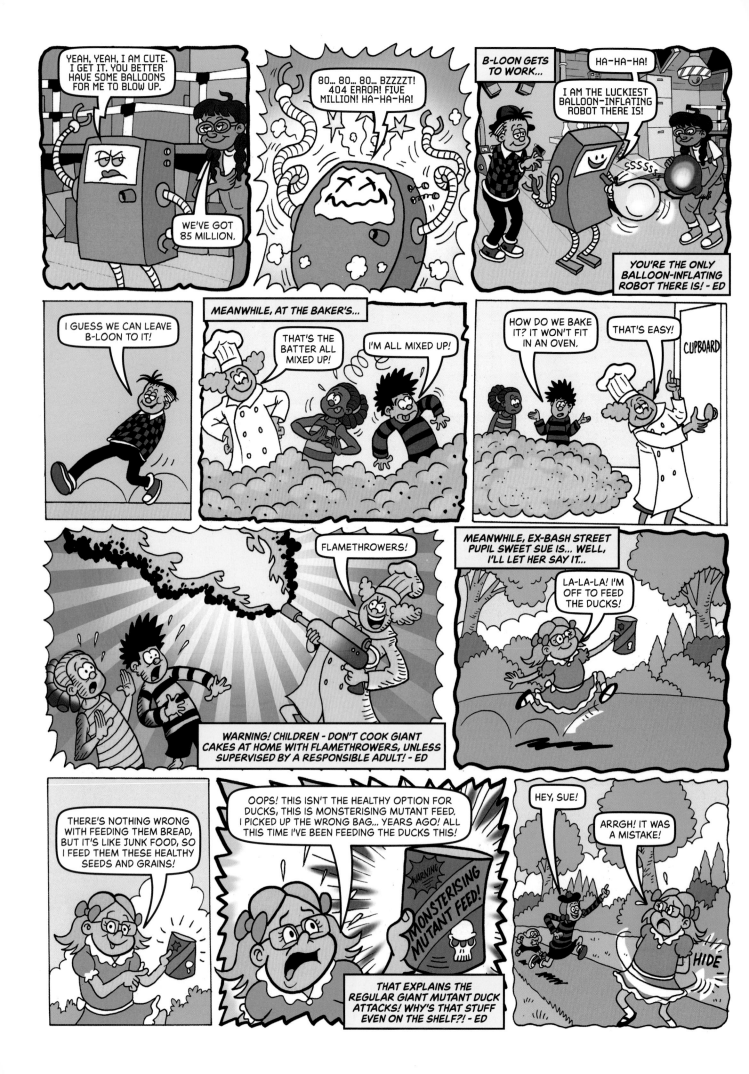

WHAT WAS A MISTAKE?

ER... WEARING THIS HAT?

WHAT HAT?

THE HAT I LOST?

DO YOU WANNA GO TO THE 85TH ANNIVERSARY OF BASH STREET SCHOOL?

I'D LOVE TO!

FLOOR IT, MAXY! WE NEED TO FIND SOMEONE CALLED PING THE ELASTIC MAN!

TAXI

WHICH ONE OF YOU IS PING THE ELASTIC MAN?

TAXI

ME!

WANNA COME TO THE 85TH ANNIVERSARY OF BASH STREET SCHOOL?

YES!

NEXT STOP, IVY THE TERRIBLE...

ARE YOU IVY THE TERRIBLE?

I'M IVY...

...BUT I'VE LEFT THE TERRIBLE BIT BEHIND, I'M NOW A SENSIBLE PERSON.

NOOOOOOO! - ED

URRGH! SOUNDS THRILLING! WANNA COME TO BASH STREET SCHOOL'S 85TH ANNIVERSARY CELEBRATION? YOU DON'T HAVE TO IF YOU DON'T WANT TO.

I'D LOVE TO COME.

FINALLY...

YOU CAN'T BE SMUDGE, THE SCRUFFIEST KID IN SCHOOL?

I'VE HAD A COMB AND WASH SINCE THEN.

WANNA, BLAH BLAH, MUMBLE?

AN 85TH ANNIVERSARY? I'D LOVE TO!

BACK AT BASH STREET SCHOOL'S SPORTS HALL...

I'VE GOT THE SPECIAL GUESTS!

BARGE!

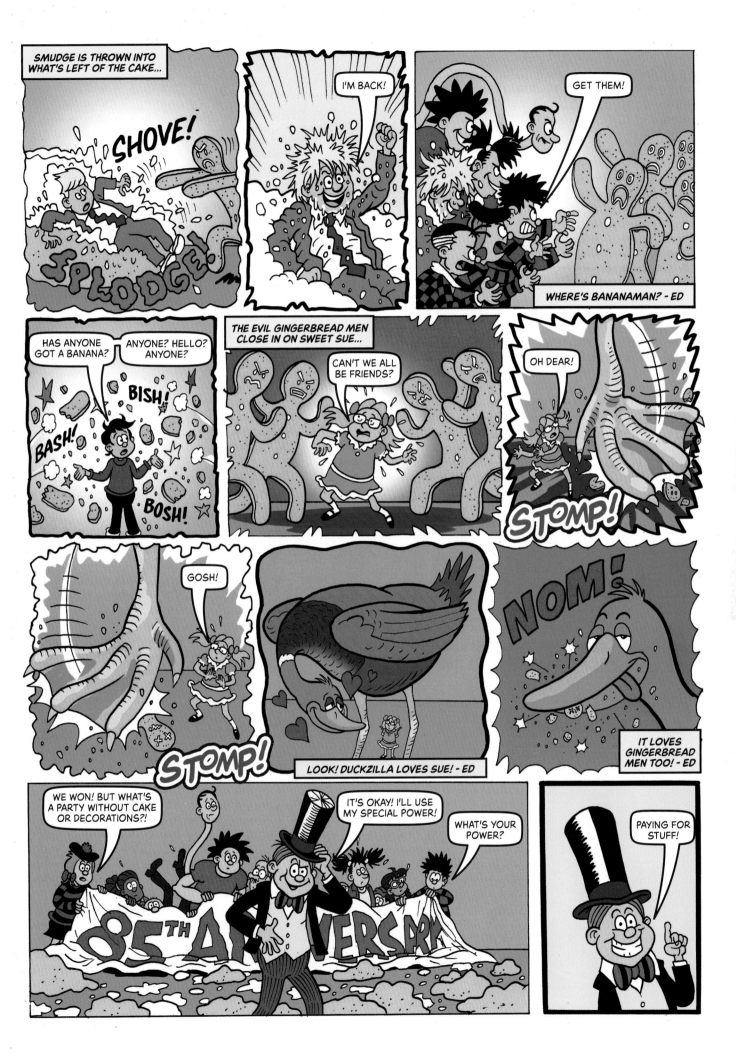

ANGEL FACE INVESTIGATES
DETECTIVE FOR HIRE!

MY HEART'S DESIRE IS TO SOLVE YOUR MYSTERY...

...BUT NOT IF IT'S STUPID!

I NEED YOU TO BE ON MY TEAM FOR THE BEANOTOWN TREASURE HUNT TODAY! WE CAN SPLIT THE PRIZE.

WHAT'S THE PRIZE?

YOUR WEIGHT IN BISCUITS!

ER... I'LL PASS, I'M A BIT SICK OF BISCUITS.

BUT THAT'S TOTALLY YOUR THING...

...OUCH! DID YOU JUST KICK ME?!

NEVER MIND - I'LL WIN WITHOUT YOUR HELP!

AT BEANOTOWN PARK...

HEY! YOU SAID YOU DIDN'T WANT TO TAKE PART!

I JUST DIDN'T WANT TO SHARE THE PRIZE!

YOU'VE ALL GOT YOUR FIRST CLUE, GET READY... ON YOUR MARKS... HUNT!

'I'M PRETTY AND SMELL SWEET. LOOK DOWN TO FIND ME, I'M NEAR YOUR FEET.' HMM, FLOWERS. THE FLOWER BEDS!

AT THE FLOWER BEDS...

NEXT CLUE - 'FULL OF WATER, BUT DON'T TAKE A SIP. WHERE FEATHERED FRIENDS TAKE A DIP.' EASY! THE DUCK POND!

YOU REALLY NEED TO STOP SHOUTING OUT THE ANSWERS!

AT THE DUCK POND...

ARRGH! WHY IS THIS SO DIFFICULT?

I'VE GOT MINE! 'THIS IS WHERE YOUR BOARD WILL LET YOU FLY, BUT YOU'LL NEED TO BE FAST TO GET THAT BISCUIT PRIZE!'

THE SKATEPARK!

THANKS, MINNIE! WHO'S SHOUTING NOW?!

THOSE BISCUITS ARE MINE!

NOT IF I GET THERE FIRST!

FINISH

YES! IT HAS TO BE ME!

NO WAY! I WAS FIRST!

SORRY, GIRLS...

...JENNY FINISHED ABOUT FIVE MINUTES AGO. SHE'S THE WINNER.

THAT'S FOR KICKING ME!

CRUMBS! WHAT A TWIST!

JJ FREEWHEELING FREESTYLE FUN!

BETTY AND THE YETI!

THE ORDINARY GIRL WITH THE EXTRAORDINARY BEST FRIEND!

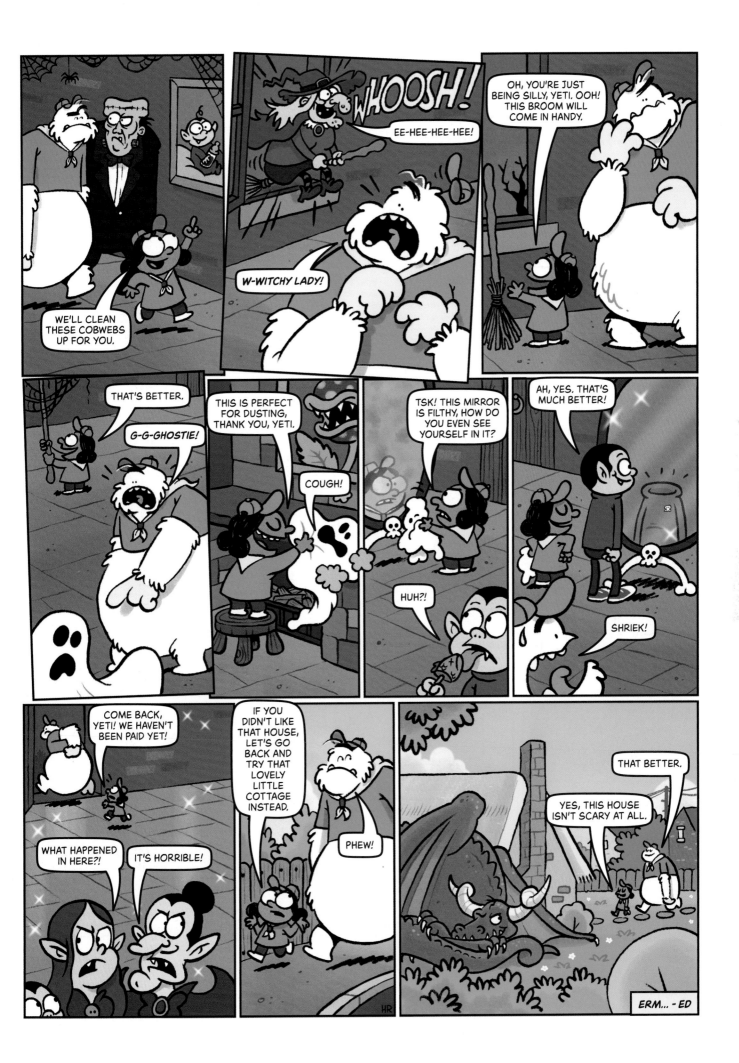

RUBI'S SCREWTOP SCIENCE

HI, RUBI, WHAT'S YOUR DAD UP TO?

IT'S AN ANTI-GRAVITY EXPERIMENT!

OOH, HOW DOES IT WORK, PROF?

ANYTHING THAT CROSSES THE LASER WILL HAVE THEIR MOLECULES 'LIGHTENED' AND WILL START TO RESIST THE DOWNWARD FORCE OF GRAVITY AND THEREBY FLOAT!

OH NO, MY PIE!

BZZT!

FIVE SECOND RULE!

WAAH!

IT WORKS!

PIE FACE!

DON'T WORRY, HE SHOULD BE FINE - AS LONG AS THE SKYLIGHT ISN'T OPEN!

AH, THE SKYLIGHT'S OPEN.

COME ON!

THE BASH STREET KIDS

TODAY WE'RE LOOKING AT ROBOTICS, AND ADVANCES IN TECHNOLOGY THAT HAVE MADE ROBOTS MORE SOPHISTICATED THAN EVER!

WHADDYA KNOW? A LESSON THAT'S ACTUALLY INTERESTING!

IN FACT, THAT GIVES ME AN IDEA.

AT BREAK TIME...

HMM... FASCINATING!

ADVANCED CYBERNETICS

HUH? WHAT IS THAT COMMOTION?

STOMP!
STOMP!
CLANG!

GREETINGS, FLESHBAG! WE ARE ROBOTS FROM THE FUTURE!

CLANG!

STOMP! STOMP!

CLANG!

BLEEP BLOOP!

HOP!

HOP!

ROBOT? I THOUGHT YOU SAID RABBIT!

I THINK YOU'LL FIND YOU ARE IN FACT CYBORGS, BECAUSE YOU'RE CLEARLY ORGANIC LIFE FORMS COMBINED WITH BIOMECHATRONIC PARTS!

YOU WHAT?

CAN I STILL BE A RABBIT?

WAY TO SPOIL OUR FUN, CUTHBERT!

YOU'LL SEE! ONE DAY MY KNOWLEDGE OF CYBER TECHNOLOGY WILL MAKE ME THE MOST POWERFUL PERSON ON THE PLANET!

WHY'D YOU HAVE TO BE SUCH A PARTY POOPER?

FZZT! FLASH!

YIKES! WHAT HAVE YOU DONE NOW?

THIS IS NOTHING TO DO WITH US! FOR A CHANGE.

I THINK THIS MINNIE IS LIKE, MY GREAT-GREAT GRANDMA OR SOMETHING!

WOW!

YOU LAUNCHED A TOMATO AT ME, YOU FIEND!

I THOUGHT YOU'D FIND IT FUNNY. YOU *ARE* A MINX, AFTER ALL!

NAH, SHE'S A GOODY-TWO-SHOES! SHE HATES MINXING!

WHAAAAT?!

I FIND IT VULGAR AND CRUDE!

ANYWAY, WE CAN'T STOP! I'VE GOT TO GET MINERVA BACK TO HER TIME, THEN I'VE GOT TO GET BACK TO MINE. IT'S BEEN NICE MEETING YOU!

NICE *MINXING* YOU!

HMPH!

HUH? THE KART ISN'T WORKING! WHAT'S WRONG WITH IT?

SPLUTTER!

MAYBE I CAN LOOK IT UP ONLINE. DO YOU HAVE A MOBILE ON YOU?

ON-WHAT? A MOBILE WHAT?

THOSE THINGS HAVEN'T BEEN INVENTED YET, MINNIE!

GAH! STUPID PAST. WE NEED SOME KIND OF *SMARTY-PANTS* TO HELP US OUT!

WE DO HAVE A SCIENTIST IN TOWN...

...PROFESSOR VON SCREWTOP!

SO...

I WONDER WHAT PROFESSOR VON SCREWTOP LOOKS LIKE IN THIS TIME?

KNOCK!

WHOA! IT'S *RUBI!*

RUBI? NO, I'M BERYL, BERYLLIUM VON SCREWTOP. CAN I HELP YOU?

WE'RE HAVING TROUBLE WITH OUR TIME MACHINE THAT YOUR GREAT-GREAT GRANDDAUGHTER INVENTED. IT'S STOPPED WORKING!

THIS WAS BUILT BY A SCREWTOP? LET ME HAVE A LOOK...

...AHA! JUST AS I THOUGHT!

DENNIS & GNASHER UNLEASHED

AS SEEN ON CBBC!

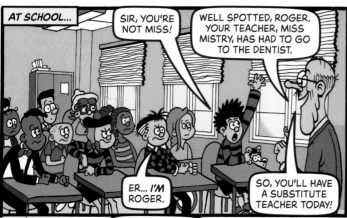

AT SCHOOL...

SIR, YOU'RE NOT MISS!

WELL SPOTTED, ROGER. YOUR TEACHER, MISS MISTRY, HAS HAD TO GO TO THE DENTIST.

ER... I'M ROGER.

SO, YOU'LL HAVE A SUBSTITUTE TEACHER TODAY!

GREAT! WE CAN GET AWAY WITH LOADS WITH A SUPPLY TEACHER!

HERE IT IS!

HELLO, CHILDREN!

A ROBOT TEACHER, ARE YOU? AN EVIL ROBOT TEACHER, YEAH? WILL THERE BE LASERS LATER?

HA-HA! NO, I AM JUST A SIMPLE TEACH-BOT HERE TO HELP YOU LEARN!

WHAT WOULD YOU LIKE TO LEARN TODAY?

IF WE GET TO CHOOSE, I CHOOSE P.E.!

HISTORY LESSON SELECTED!

NO, P.E.!

SCIENCE LESSON SELECTED!

HA-HA! I AM KIDDING! I KNOW YOU ARE ASKING FOR P.E.!

THAT IS A LITTLE BIT OF ROBOT HUMOUR THERE.

YOU KNOW, A JOKE ABOUT HOW SOMETIMES BLUETOOTH SPEAKERS GET WHAT YOU SAY WRONG.

HELLO? ANYONE? TOUGH CROWD!

DENNIS SNEAKS BEHIND TEACH-BOT...

6728 AA BATTERIES

OFF

IF I CAN FIND THE OFF SWITCH, WE CAN ALL CHILL TILL LUNCHTIME!

THERE IT IS!

OFF

ATTACK DETECTED! AWOOGA! ALERT!

HOLD ON! I WASN'T...

ACTIVATE DEFENCE MODE! BRINGING LASERS ONLINE!

LASERS?!

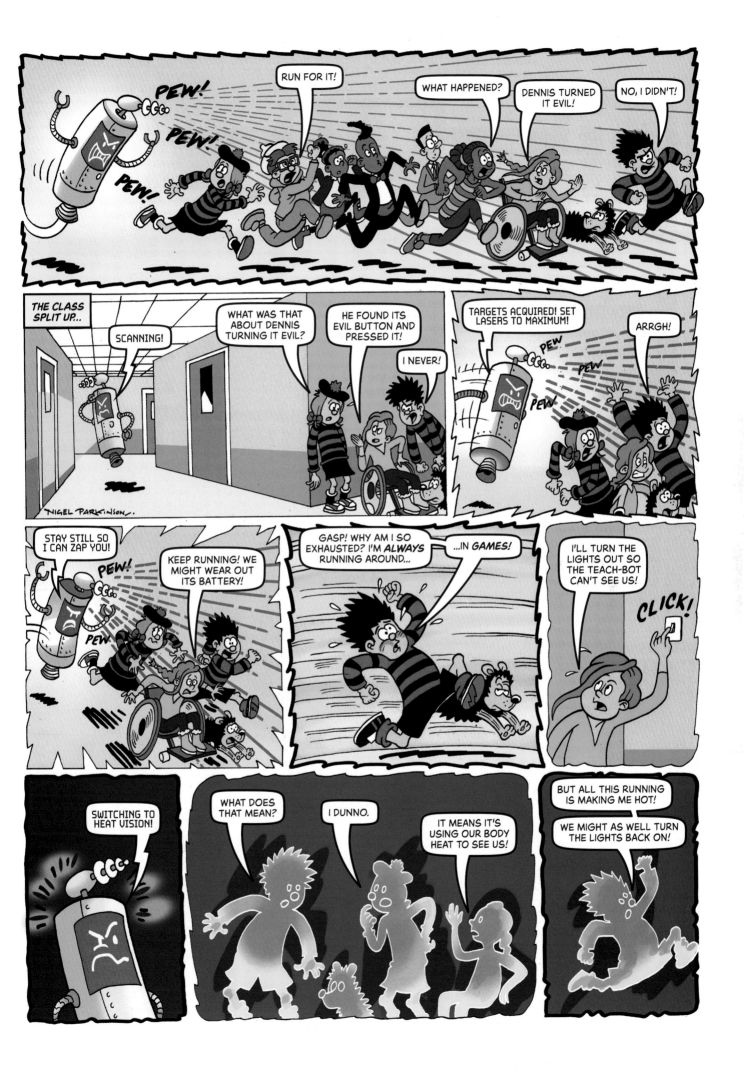

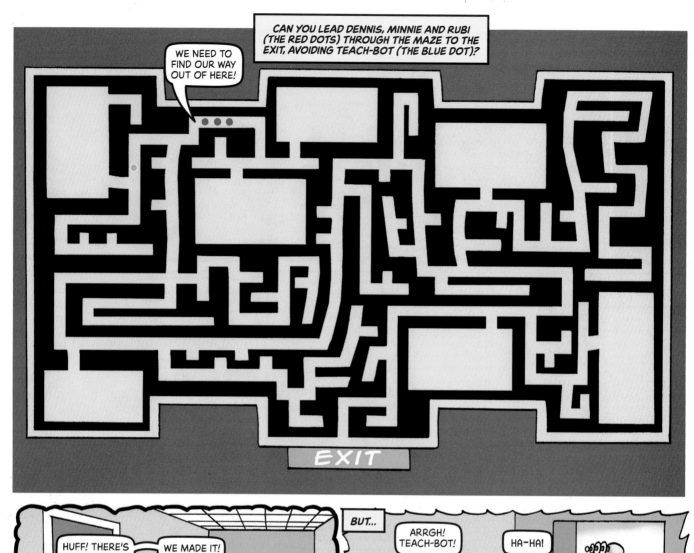

WHEN LITTLE ERIC EATS A BANANA, HE BECOMES...
BANANAMAN

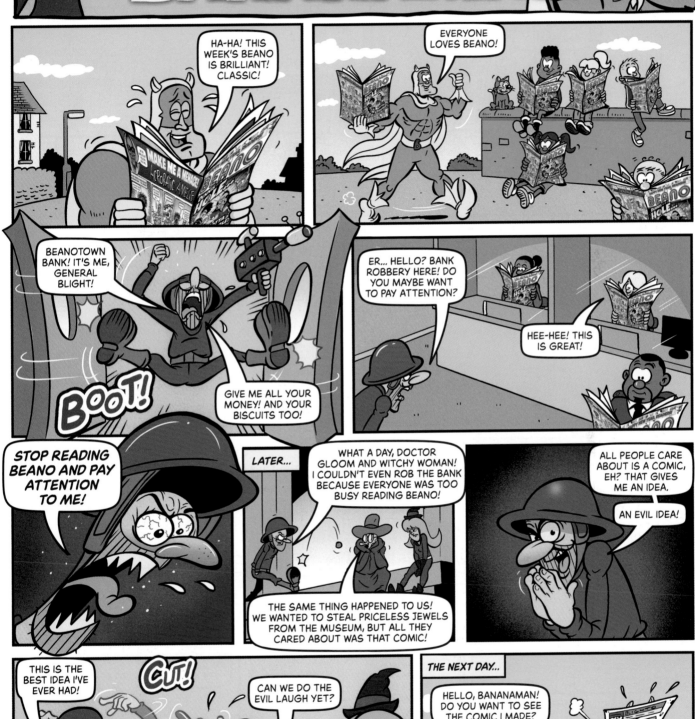

HA-HA! THIS WEEK'S BEANO IS BRILLIANT! CLASSIC!

EVERYONE LOVES BEANO!

BEANOTOWN BANK! IT'S ME, GENERAL BLIGHT!

BOOT!

GIVE ME ALL YOUR MONEY! AND YOUR BISCUITS TOO!

ER... HELLO? BANK ROBBERY HERE! DO YOU MAYBE WANT TO PAY ATTENTION?

HEE-HEE! THIS IS GREAT!

STOP READING BEANO AND PAY ATTENTION TO ME!

LATER...

WHAT A DAY, DOCTOR GLOOM AND WITCHY WOMAN! I COULDN'T EVEN ROB THE BANK BECAUSE EVERYONE WAS TOO BUSY READING BEANO!

THE SAME THING HAPPENED TO US! WE WANTED TO STEAL PRICELESS JEWELS FROM THE MUSEUM, BUT ALL THEY CARED ABOUT WAS THAT COMIC!

ALL PEOPLE CARE ABOUT IS A COMIC, EH? THAT GIVES ME AN IDEA.

AN EVIL IDEA!

THIS IS THE BEST IDEA I'VE EVER HAD!

CUT!

DRAW!

WRITE!

CAN WE DO THE EVIL LAUGH YET?

NO, WE'LL DO IT LATER.

THE NEXT DAY...

HELLO, BANANAMAN! DO YOU WANT TO SEE THE COMIC I MADE?

'BLIGHTO'? WHAT'S THIS?

SHE'S BEHIND ME, ISN'T SHE?

BERET.

HERE YOU GO, PLEASE DON'T HURT ME.

RESPECT INTELLECTUAL COPYRIGHT!

SPLAT!

WHO ELSE DOES 'BLIGHTO' HAVE IN IT, THEN?

THERE IS ONE MORE CHARACTER.

I REALLY DON'T WANT TO DO THIS...

...BLIGHT-NANA-MAN!

YEAH, THIS WAS A BAD IDEA.

DO YOU HAVE ANY POWERS?

I THINK MY ONLY POWER SHOULD BE THAT I CAN PRETEND THIS NEVER HAPPENED.

YOU KNOW, THERE'S A MUCH EASIER WAY TO READ A GREAT COMIC.

THERE IS?

JUST BUY BEANO EVERY WEEK!

HEE-HEE! THIS IS ACTUALLY REALLY GOOD!

DID YOU SEE THIS BIT? TEE-HEE!

I LOVE THE READER LETTERS!

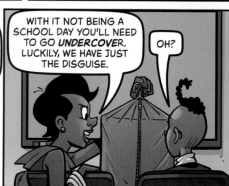

AND SO...

NOW I FEEL EVEN MORE STUPID!

HACKBOT LOOKS LIKE FLESHY, HUMAN CHILD! WHEEE!

THERE'S THE PREFECT. HE THINKS I CAN'T SEE THROUGH HIS LAME DISGUISE! AND THERE'S HIS COMPUTER! ACT *NATURAL*, HACKBOT!

AFFIRMATIVE!

THANK YOU FOR DONATING THIS COMPUTER, MR, ER... PREFECT! IT'S SO KIND!

NOT AT ALL! I'M HAPPY TO HELP THE COMMUNITY! HEH-HEH!

HELLO! I DON'T BELIEVE WE'VE BEEN INTRODUCED.

I'M, ER... DANGEROUS D... *DEREK*. AND THIS IS MY GRANDSON, BERTIE.

AFFIRMATIVE!

UNUSUAL LOOKING LAD, ISN'T HE?

I AM A NORMAL HUMAN BOY CHILD!

FAIR ENOUGH, ENJOY THE CEREMONY!

I THINK WE GOT AWAY WITH IT, HACKBOT!

HACKBOT?! WHAT ARE YOU DOING? WE NEED TO FOCUS ON THE MISSION!

NEGATIVE! HACKBOT IS ONLY INTERESTED IN BOUNCING NOW!

IF IT'S BOUNCING YOU WANT, IT'S BOUNCING YOU'LL GET!

BOUNCE!

WHEEEE! I AM FLYING!

LAND!

UPDATE – I AM NO LONGER FLYING!

MY COMPUTER!

HOW WILL I TAKE OVER THE TOWN NOW?

LOOKS LIKE THE PREFECT'S COMPUTER SUFFERED A *CRASH*! CHUCKLE! COME ON, HACKBOT!

HACKBOT WANTS ONE MORE GO!

HAR HAR'S JOKE SHOP!

MEET BEANOTOWN'S FUNNIEST FAMILY!

HARI · SAHANA · HEENA · HARSHA · HANI

WHAT?! SOMEONE LEFT US A **ONE-STAR REVIEW** ON 'SHOP ADVISOR'! THEY SAY WE'RE, 'JUST A SILLY, SMELLY JOKE SHOP!'

DON'T WORRY ABOUT THEM, DAD.

WHERE SHALL WE PUT THESE SPARE CHILLI SWEETS?

JUST STICK THEM IN THE STOREROOM, SIGH...

THE SHELVES ARE ALL FULL.

MAYBE TRY FURTHER TOWARDS THE BACK.

THIS IS MUCH LONGER THAN IT LOOKS FROM THE OUTSIDE!

I DIDN'T KNOW WE SOLD **NORMAL** SWEETS.

WE DON'T, THAT'S WEIRD.

THERE'S A DOOR BACK HERE.

OOH! OPEN IT!

WHOA! IT'S A **SWEET SHOP!**

WHO ARE YOU AND WHAT WERE YOU DOING IN OUR STOREROOM?

YOUR STOREROOM? THAT'S **OUR** STOREROOM!

WAIT... WHERE ARE YOU FROM?

HAR HAR'S JOKE SHOP, 'WHERE YOUR LAUGHTER IS PAYMENT ENOUGH FOR US... PLUS ACTUAL MONEY.'

IT'S SO WEIRD THAT WE SHARE A STOREROOM.

URRGH! THAT PLACE! WE WENT THERE LAST WEEK. IT'S SO DINGY AND SMELLY!

THIS IS 'JAR JAR'S SWEET SHOP', A SOPHISTICATED SELECTION OF CONFECTIONERY FOR THE DISCERNING SHOPPER.

WHAT LANGUAGE IS THAT?!

SMARTY PANT-ESE, I THINK!

THIS IS WHAT A PROPER SHOP LOOKS LIKE, BRIGHT, CLEAN AND FULL OF HIGH-QUALITY PRODUCTS.

NOT LIKE THAT RUBBISH SHOP YOU HAVE!

HEY! YOU'RE NOT BEING VERY SWEET!

WE HAVE 100% RATING ON 'SHOP ADVISOR' TO PROVE IT, UNLIKE YOU!

IT'S TRUE, THIS CUSTOMER CALLS IT, 'A DREAM COME TRUE!'

PFFT! IT'S MORE LIKE A NIGHTMARE!

AND OUR DAD WAS THE ONE WHO LEFT YOU AND YOUR PATHETIC SHOP A ONE-STAR REVIEW.

HA-HA-HA!

DUN-DUN-DUN!

WHAT A TWIST!

NO-ONE CAN DEFEAT US AND OUR PERFECT FIVE-STAR RATING!

NEXT STOP... WE TAKE OVER THE WORLD!

THEY'RE REALLY WEIRD ABOUT THEIR CUSTOMER RATINGS. LET'S GO!

BUT ON THE WAY BACK OUT...

OOPS!

BUMP

WELL, WE WON'T BE GOING BACK THERE AGAIN! THEY WERE SO RUDE... AND I'M PRETTY SURE THEY WERE ALSO PURE EVIL!

I DON'T THINK WE CAN ANYWAY - THE FALLEN STOCK HAS SEALED IT OFF!

BACK IN THE SHOP...

HOW ARE YOU FEELING, DAD?

MUCH BETTER, THANKS. WE DON'T NEED THE BEST SHOP RATINGS - WE'RE PERFECT THE WAY WE ARE!

I WANTED TO LEAVE JAR JAR'S A NEGATIVE REVIEW AFTER ALL THAT, BUT DAD'S MADE ME SEE THAT THE SWEETEST REVENGE IS JUST BEING HAPPY!

ERM... WHERE DID WE LEAVE THOSE JARS OF MEGA HOT CHILLI SWEETS?

BACK AT JAR JAR'S...

SHRIEK! MY MOUTH IS ON FIRE!

NOOOOO!

I QUITE LIKE THEM BUT I'M KNOCKING A COUPLE OF STARS OFF FOR ALL THE SCREAMING.

HARSHA'S PRANK ACADEMY

ALLERGY AWARE! Do not try this prank where allergies may be an issue.

YOU'LL EAT THIS SPONGE TRICK RIGHT UP!

You'll need: ■ A thick slice of bread ■ Green and yellow food gel colour ■ Two paintbrushes

1

Ask an adult to cut the slice of bread into a square for you. Put some of the yellow food gel colour onto the brush and paint it all over the bread.

2

Use the green food gel colour and dab it onto the top side of the bread to look like the top of a sponge.

3

I'M SO HUNGRY, I COULD EAT ANYTHING!

Swap the bread with your kitchen sponge and tell the person you're pranking that you're hungry.

4

Instead of grabbing a snack, pick up the 'kitchen sponge' and take a bite – they will be so **soap-rised**!

ANGEL FACE INVESTIGATES DETECTIVE FOR HIRE!

ANGEL FACE INVESTIGATIONS. WHERE YOU COME WHEN YOU CAN'T AFFORD ANYONE ELSE.

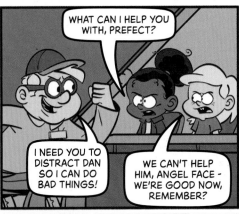

WHAT CAN I HELP YOU WITH, PREFECT?

I NEED YOU TO DISTRACT DAN SO I CAN DO BAD THINGS!

WE CAN'T HELP HIM, ANGEL FACE - WE'RE GOOD NOW, REMEMBER?

WE'LL DO IT!

NO!

PERFECT!

THE NEXT DAY...

THERE'S DAN! WHY IS HE CLIMBING INTO THAT BIN?!

LET'S FOLLOW HIM!

INSIDE THE BIN...

WHOA! ARE YOU A SPY, DAN? I WANNA BE A SPY!

YOU CAN'T BE HERE! WHERE'S MY MEMORY WIPER?!

WAIT! WE CAN HELP! I'M THE SNEAKIEST PERSON I KNOW!

OKAY - THIS MISSION COULD ACTUALLY USE MORE PEOPLE. YOU'VE TO PROTECT THE EYE OF BEANOTOWN DIAMOND IN THE MUSEUM FROM THE PREFECT.

SOUNDS EASY!

SO...

OH NO! MY MOTOR'S JAMMED! GO ON WITHOUT ME, ANGEL FACE!

I WONDER HOW THAT HAPPENED?! SNIGGER!

SORRY, DAN, BUT THIS IS TOO GOOD AN OPPORTUNITY TO MISS!

ANGEL FACE! NO!

SWIPE!

I CAN'T WAIT TO CHARGE THE PREFECT EXTRA FOR DISTRACTING DAN AND SWIPING THE DIAMOND!

THAT WAS REALLY MEAN SABOTAGING DAN'S HARNESS LIKE THAT!

I'LL BE TAKING THAT, THANKS. I KNEW YOU'D BE TROUBLE. SAY GOODBYE TO YOUR MEMORIES OF THE LAST HOUR!

EW! WHY DO YOU SMELL LIKE A BIN, JENNY?

I DUNNO!

NUMSKULLS

The Little people that Live in your head! Everybody has them!

THERE'S A LOT GOING ON IN EDD'S HEAD...

NO, THERE'S NOT.

I THINK THE OTHERS ARE OUT.

MEANWHILE, IN PLUG'S EAR...

CAN YOU STOP EATING THAT?!

I DON'T THINK I CAN.

THERE'S A LIGHT UP AHEAD! WE'VE MADE IT!

URRGH! WE MUST HAVE TAKEN A WRONG TURN!

JUMP!

I'M NOT GOING BACK!

THERE'S A LOT GOING ON IN TOOTS' HEAD...

THIS IS OUR HEAD NOW!

TOOTS' HEAD TO SIDNEY'S HEAD, COME IN, OVER.

WHAT DO YOU WANT? DO IT YOURSELF, WHATEVER IT IS.

IT'S SO LAME HAVING A TWIN SISTER, I'D RATHER HAVE A CAT, AND I DON'T LIKE CATS.

I'LL NEVER HELP YOU.

PIRATE NUMSKULLS ARE ATTACKING!

WHAT?! NO-ONE MESSES WITH MY SISTER!

SIDNEY'S NUMSKULLS GANG UP WITH TOOTS' NUMSKULLS AGAINST EDD'S...

AT LEAST THEY CALLED US PIRATES!

YEAH, THAT WAS COOL! OW!

BLSH!

BOSH!

EDD'S NUMSKULLS ESCAPE TO HARSHA'S HEAD...

JUMP!

THERE'S A LOT GOING ON IN HARSHA'S HEAD...

JUST GO EASY, OKAY? WE DON'T WANT ANY TROUBLE.

YOU LOOK WORN OUT. COME IN, SIT DOWN AND HAVE A REST.

ROGER THE DODGER

HE'S ALWAYS GOT A TRICK UP HIS SLEEVE!

MONDAY MORNING...

MUM! I'M OUT OF JUMPERS!

I'VE LEFT ONE ON THE BED FOR YOU.

OH NO! ANYTHING BUT THAT!

DOWNSTAIRS...

I CAN'T BE SEEN WEARING THIS HIDEOUS ITCH-FEST.

ALL YOUR OTHER JUMPERS ARE IN THE WASH. WEAR THAT OLD ONE FOR TODAY.

I FEEL LIKE I'M BEING STITCHED UP.

WRIGGLE!

STOP COMPLAINING AND GET TO SCHOOL.

SO...

IT'S A BIT HOT FOR A COAT, ROGER.

I NEED TO KEEP MYSELF WRAPPED UP TODAY.

HAND OVER YOUR LUNCHES, LOSERS.

BUT KEEP ANY FRUIT!

QUICK, ROGER, WE NEED A DODGE.

I COULD TRY, ERM... DODGE...

SWEAT! TREMBLE!

WHY'S YOUR FACE TURNING RED?

WHAT'S THE MATTER, ROGER?

STEAM! SWEAT!

THANKS FOR THE LUNCH!

I DON'T KNOW WHAT HAPPENED. I COULDN'T THINK OF A SINGLE DODGE.

IT MUST BE THIS STUPID JUMPER. I JUST DON'T FEEL THE SAME WITHOUT MY REGULAR ONE.

GASP! YOU'VE LOST YOUR DODGE POWERS!

AT SCHOOL...

MR DAWSON! SCHOOL RULE #3009CT - NO WEARING OF OUTDOOR COATS INSIDE THE BUILDING.

BUT I'M COLD.

REMOVE YOUR COAT AT ONCE!

COME ON, ROGER, YOU CAN THINK OF A DODGE TO GET OUT OF THIS.

GNNNGH! THINK... THINK...

...SIGH! I CAN'T THINK OF A SINGLE DODGE.

HA-HA!

GRUMBLE! THE WOOL IN THIS JUMPER IS UN-BAA-RABLE.

ITCH! ITCH! ITCH!

ITCH! ITCH!

I CAN'T... TAKE... MUCH MORE OF THIS!

ROGER, CAN YOU COME TO THE FRONT OF THE CLASS AND READ OUT THE REPORT I SET YOU FOR HOMEWORK?

GULP!

OH NO! I DIDN'T DO MY HOMEWORK.

OF COURSE, MISS. BUT I NEED TO GO TO THE TOILET FIRST. I FEEL A LITTLE *FLUSH*.

OKAY, BUT HURRY BACK.

WHOOSH!

RUB!

MRS YODEL'S OFFICE

COME ON, BRAIN. THINK OF A DODGE!

YODEL'S OFFICE

LOST PROPERTY

THAT'S IT! TIME TO *CHANGE* MY FORTUNES WITH... DODGE 789LP.

PERFECT! I KNEW I'D FIND ONE OF DENNIS'S JUMPERS IN HERE.

I JUST NEED TO MAKE A FEW ADJUSTMENTS.

LOST

NOW IT'S TIME TO *JUMP* INTO THIS NEW JUMPER.

SQIGGLE!

RED

SHINE!

I'M BACK AND READY TO READ MY REPORT, MISS.

WOW!

SOMEHOW, 30 MINUTES LATER...

YOU DODGED THE WHOLE SCHOOL OUT OF LESSONS AND INTO BEANOTOWN CINEMA FOR FREE, WITH LIMITLESS POPCORN *AND* DRINKS!

IT'S GOOD TO HAVE YOU BACK, ROGER.

HA! I JUST NEEDED A *CHANGE*.

EXIT

FART WARS!

JJ FREEWHEELING FREESTYLE FUN!

MY WEEK IS SO FULL OF AFTER-SCHOOL ACTIVITIES! LUCKILY, I HAVE EVERYTHING PLANNED OUT ON MY PHONE!

TAP!

ARRGH! I *DELETED* EVERYTHING!

BLOOP!

I'M SURE IT WILL BE FINE! I'VE GOT EVERYTHING MEMORISED ANYWAY...

ON MONDAY...

BOUNCE!

BOUNCE!

OOPS! I PACKED THE WRONG STUFF IN MY BOWLING BAG!

ON TUESDAY...

I COULD HAVE SWORN IT WAS RUGBY TONIGHT!

SPLAT!

EW!

ON WEDNESDAY...

HMM... RUGBY'S NOT TONIGHT EITHER!

THONK!

ON THURSDAY...

OUCH! SO THAT'S WHERE MY BOWLING BALL AND CLOTHES WENT - MY FOOTBALL BAG!

CLANG!

ON FRIDAY...

THIS IS A WEIRD WEEK FOR ME!

FUMBLE!

ON SATURDAY...

OUCH! OH, YEAH... BALLET WAS ON WEDNESDAY, RIGHT?

CLOSE BUT NOT QUITE, JJ! - ED

THE NEXT MONDAY...

THIS WEEK, I'M NOT GOING TO MISS ANYTHING...

...I'M PREPARED FOR ALL THE SPORTS!

CALAMITY JAMES

THE UNLUCKIEST BOY IN THE WORLD!